Letoya — All Eyez

Its So Hard (2000)
— Big Pun/Donell Jones

Aint No future in Yo Frontin
M.C. Breed/DFC

The overweight Lovers in the House
— Heavy D & the Boyz

One Wish   Here comes
— Ray J   the Hammer
                   — MC Hammer

Soul Survivor
by: Young Jeezy

Youngbloodz
— PRESIDENTAL

BOOK F
BASIC READING

GLENN McCRACKEN
New Castle, Pennsylvania

CHARLES C. WALCUTT
Queens College, Flushing, New York

J. B. LIPPINCOTT COMPANY
PHILADELPHIA, NEW YORK

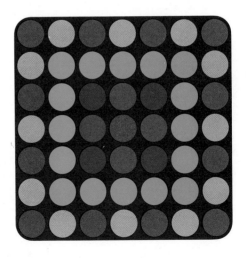

CONTENTS

Part 1 — Horses, Boys, and Eagles

Part 2 — We Visit

Poems

58.775.6

Part 3 — Fun With Animals

Poems

Part 4 — Learning to Work and Play

Poems

Part 5 — Famous American Women

Poems

Part 6 — Famous Women of Other Lands

Poems

PART 1

Horses
Boys
and
Eagles

1

Lightning, A Cowboy's Colt

Up the Mountain Trail

Danny Morgan was a boy who lived on a ranch. His father, Brick Morgan, owned the ranch. They lived at a time when there were many Indians.

One day, Danny and his father rode up a mountain trail. Danny talked excitedly. The ride to Lookout Point was fun for Danny because it was near an Indian camp.

"Lightning, A Cowboy's Colt" adapted from *Lightning, A Cowboy's Colt* by Bill and Bernard Martin. Copyright 1948 by Bernard H. Martin and William I. Martin, Jr. Reprinted by permission of Holt, Rinehart and Winston, Inc.

"Father, after we ride to the Point, let's go over to the Indian camp," Danny said eagerly.

"No, Danny. I'm afraid there won't be time today," Brick Morgan answered.

Danny liked Indians. All the way up the trail, he hoped he would meet some Indian boys on their spotted ponies.

"Look! There's Golden Boy!" Danny said suddenly. He pointed to a tiny speck racing across the fields.

Danny's heart pounded. The sight of Golden Boy always excited him. The big horse was leader of the Morgan herd of horses.

"When will you go after the horses?" asked Danny, hoping that he could go with his father and the cowboys on the spring roundup.

"We start next week," Brick Morgan answered. "I wish I could take you along, Partner, but someone has to stay at home to feed the animals."

Danny felt sad that he could not go along.

"Be a good boy," his father said. "I may have a surprise for you when I come back."

"A colt? Will it be a colt, Father?"

"It wouldn't be a surprise if I told you," his father laughed.

A Surprise

Weeks passed before the roundup was over. When Brick Morgan returned home, Danny ran to meet him and jumped into his father's strong arms.

"Did you bring me a colt, Father? Is it a colt?" asked Danny.

Yes, it was a colt. Danny was to have his choice of any colt in the herd. As he raced to the corral to see the horses, Danny was a streak of leaping joy.

He hung on the corral gate and wondered how he could ever choose just one colt for his own. He loved every horse and colt in the herd.

Danny looked carefully at the long-legged colts. He thought he wanted a colt, but there was a horse that excited him each time he saw her. She was as beautiful as Golden Boy. She was a young mare, black and fast, with small, fine ears that pointed straight ahead. Danny thought he had never seen a more beautiful horse. He chose her.

"She's your horse now, Danny," said Brick Morgan. "Take good care of her and she will always take care of you."

"I will, Father, I promise I will." Danny danced in excitement. "Do you think she knows me yet?"

The mare was a truly fine horse. Brick Morgan looked carefully at her. Then he noticed something strange. The mare was not branded. There was no mark on her to show who owned her.

"Where did this mare come from?" Brick Morgan shouted to Slim, the ranch foreman. "She isn't ours!"

Danny's heart pounded in fear. The black mare was his. She had to be his. "Oh, please let her be mine," he thought. "Don't take her away from me, Father."

"I've never seen the mare before," Slim answered. "She must have joined our herd during the winter."

"That makes her ours, doesn't it, Father?" said Danny. "She's ours now, isn't she?"

"Yes, the law of the range says she is our mare," said Brick. "Nobody else has branded her to prove ownership, and she is with our herd. I guess we can keep her."

Danny laughed for joy. The mare was his. She would always be his. He would have her branded when the cowboys branded the colts.

Danny watered and fed the black mare with a love that a boy has only for his horse. He brought her sugar and apples and cool water. He gave her more oats and hay than she could eat. But the black mare was not very friendly to Danny. She did not let him get close to her.

Angry Indians

One afternoon Danny went to the stream to get her some fresh water. When he dipped the bucket into the water, the stream looked so cool that he wished he were in it. Quickly, he pulled off his boots and in he splashed.

Suddenly, in the distance, he heard his father shout for Slim. By the sound of his voice, Danny knew that something was wrong. He scrambled up to the top of a big rock and looked toward the barn. A group of Indians at the barn were pointing angrily at the black mare as they talked with his father.

Danny jumped from the rock and ran up the stream. Sharp stones cut his feet, but he was too excited to feel them. Finding his boots, he pulled them on quickly. Then he grabbed the bucket and headed for the barn. Just as he reached the barn, the Indians were riding away.

"What's the matter, Father?" shouted Danny.

"The Indians came for the mare," his father said.

"Are they going to take her away?" asked Danny.

"No," said his father. "I don't think this mare is an Indian pony. And she doesn't seem to have a brand. We'll wait to see who really owns her."

Danny Meets Eagle

Two nights later, Danny went out to tell his horse good night. He saw her standing away from the herd, all by herself. She was very quiet as if she had expected him to come.

"She knows me!" thought Danny. "She knows me now." The mare had never been friendly with Danny, but he thought she acted friendly now.

As he came closer, he saw that someone else was standing beside the mare. It was a boy. An Indian boy!

"What are you doing here?" Danny called out.

"I've come to see my horse," said the Indian boy.

"Your horse? She isn't. She's not branded," said Danny.

"This is my horse, Star Fire," the Indian said. "See how she knows me?"

The black mare was rubbing the Indian's hand with her nose. She stood quietly as he petted and stroked her.

"But—but—you didn't brand her," Danny gasped.

"I didn't brand Star Fire," said the Indian boy. "A brand doesn't make her mine. Friendship makes her mine. She will always be mine no matter where she goes."

Danny felt very sad. He knew that the mare must belong to the Indian because she was so friendly with him. She would never let Danny pet her.

"What's your name?" asked Danny.

"I am Eagle," said the Indian. "What do they call you?"

"Danny," said Danny.

There was so much love in the way Eagle petted Star Fire that Danny was no longer afraid.

"Did you miss her while she was gone?" he asked.

Eagle nodded his head. "I want Star Fire home again."

Danny said, "Take your horse, Eagle. If she is yours she could never belong to me— not really."

As Eagle rode Star Fire away, he called back to Danny, "Thank you, Danny. Star Fire and Eagle will never forget."

Danny Tells His Father

Danny felt lonely and tired as he watched the Indian ride down the trail. Star Fire was gone. The beautiful black mare that he loved belonged to someone else.

Danny sat at the breakfast table the next morning, waiting for his father to finish eating. Then he said quickly, "Star Fire is gone, Father. I gave her away."

Brick Morgan looked at Danny. "Star Fire?"

"The black mare," said Danny. "I gave her away."

"You what?" said his father in a voice full of surprise.

"I gave her to Eagle," Danny told him. "He's an Indian. She was his horse. He came to see her last night, and I told him to take her."

"Did Eagle say she was his horse?" asked Brick Morgan.

"Yes, but Eagle didn't have to tell me that she was his horse," said Danny.

"Star Fire told me. She told me by the way she loved him and licked his hand. Horses don't lie, do they, Father? Do they?"

Brick Morgan didn't say another word. He grabbed his hat and walked out of the house. He was sorry that Danny had lost the horse he loved so much.

Eagle Returns

One evening the following summer, Danny was up in the barn. Suddenly he heard a little pebble hit on the roof. Looking out, he saw Eagle motioning for him to come out. He hadn't seen Eagle since he had come for Star Fire many months ago.

Danny quickly dropped to the ground.

"Come with me," Eagle said. "Star Fire and Eagle have a surprise for you." Eagle jumped on Star Fire's back and helped Danny up behind him.

"Are you going to the Indian camp?" Danny asked. "I've never been there."

"Indians are your friends," Eagle said kindly. "Don't be afraid."

When they rode into the camp, Danny slipped down from Star Fire's back and followed Eagle past some tepees.

"Look!" Eagle whispered. He pointed to a young colt in the shadows among some trees. "That's Star Fire's colt," said Eagle. "My father, Chief Eagle Feather, and I give him to you."

19

"To me?" Danny stopped and looked at the beautiful, soft red colt. He reached out and touched the colt's silken coat. The colt liked Danny and licked his hand. Danny put his arms around its neck and pressed his head against it.

The colt had a white mark on its forehead. It was just like the mark on Golden Boy's forehead.

Lightning, Son of Star Fire

"See how the white mark flashes, Eagle?" Danny cried. "I think I'll call my colt Lightning—Lightning, son of Star Fire."

"You ride Star Fire home. Your colt will follow," Eagle said. "I'll ride my father's white horse and bring Star Fire back."

The next morning Brick Morgan found Danny sitting on the grass. Beside him lay a beautiful colt. The colt and the boy jumped up. The colt was all legs as it scrambled to its feet.

"Look, Father! He's mine!" Danny called out. "He's Lightning! He's my colt! Eagle gave him to me. Star Fire had a colt and Eagle gave him to me. And he's got a mark on his head just like Golden Boy. See!"

"Oh, he's a beautiful colt, Danny!" said his mother, coming from the house. "I hope you will let him keep the colt, Brick."

In Brick Morgan's smile, Danny found the answer he wanted. "He's going to let me keep him!" Danny shouted. "He's going let me keep Lightning!"

Gray Fox and the Eagles

A Boy's Dream

Gray Fox was a little Indian boy. His father was Big Chief Beaver. Gray Fox dreamed of the time when he would be big enough to go hunting with the braves.

One evening the Indian braves sat close around the fire. Big Chief Beaver quietly smoked a pipe. Tomorrow they would start on the big hunt.

23

Young Gray Fox sat in the outer circle. He watched the smoke from the campfire curling lazily on its way up to the sky. He listened to the tales of the hunt. The braves had many stories to tell of their great skills in hunting.

Soon the fires burned low. The braves left, one by one, to rest before their long journey. Before sun-up they would be well along the trail.

Gray Fox waited until the last Indian brave had left the campfire. Then he crawled over and sat down beside his father, Big Chief Beaver.

24

"Father," said Gray Fox, "I too wish to hunt with the braves. I am strong. My arrow shoots more swiftly than the wind."

"Even the son of a chief must prove his courage before he can hunt with the braves," said his father. "First you must bring me a feather pulled from the tail of a fierce live eagle. Only then can you go on the hunt."

Early the next morning, Gray Fox started on his long, difficult search for the nest of the mighty eagle. He knew it would be hidden high up on the mountain.

He walked many days before he reached
the foot of the mountain. After more days
of climbing, he was so high up the mountain
that no trees grew there. Now he went
more slowly. He picked his way carefully,
examining the rough cliffs and ledges with
his keen eyes.

Gray Fox Helps the Eagles

Then he saw it! High up on a rocky ledge was a nest of twigs and branches.

Gray Fox climbed the sharp rocks until he was above the eagle's nest. He looked down. Something was wrong. The two baby eagles in the nest looked sick, their heads hung low. Beside the nest, on a ledge, was a wounded mother eagle. An arrow had pierced her wing. The broken shaft was still stuck in it.

Gray Fox knew in an instant that trouble had struck the eagle family. The father eagle was most likely dead, for the baby eagles were starving. The great mother eagle lay helplessly on the ledge, keeping watch on her hungry babies but not able to hunt and bring them food.

Gray Fox climbed back along the cliff. He knew what must be done. He had seen the signs left by passing animals and knew a jackrabbit was nearby.

There it was! A perfect target standing on a rock. Gray Fox took a stone from his belt. He threw it. Straight and true the stone traveled and the rabbit fell dead.

Then Gray Fox carried the rabbit over the rocky trail above the ledge. Slowly he climbed down until he reached the eagle's nest. He put the rabbit down, took his knife, and skinned the animal. Then he cut strips of meat and fed the young eagles.

The mother eagle, though weak, helpless, and very near death, tried in vain to struggle toward him, ready to protect her young eagles. Gray Fox continued to feed them, being careful to stay out of reach of the mother eagle's beak and claws.

Then slowly the mother eagle began to understand that Gray Fox would not harm her baby eagles. She stopped trying to get to them and watched quietly while they were fed.

Gray Fox was watching her. Now he was sure she would not harm him. With no thought of danger, he cut a strip of meat and gave it to the mother eagle. While she ate, Gray Fox pulled the broken arrow from her wing. Then he set the broken wing, using strong twigs to brace it and coarse grass to tie it in place.

For several weeks, Gray Fox stayed with the eagles. He went out each day to hunt for their food. But there came a day when he hunted long and far in search of food. Toward sundown he started back, empty-handed. As he neared the nest, he heard the cry of a mountain lion. Gray Fox ran swiftly, thinking only of the danger to his eagles.

When he neared the rocks above the nest, he saw the lion, pacing back and forth. Gray Fox silently drew his bow. He took an arrow and aimed carefully. Swiftly the arrow flew and buried itself in the big cat's back. The animal, enraged with pain, leaped toward Gray Fox in snarling fury. But again an arrow flew. It hit deep in the animal's shoulder and made him stumble in his tracks.

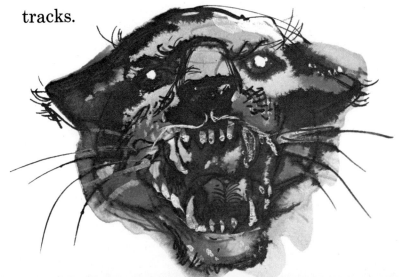

Gray Fox started to circle toward the rock above the ledge. But before he reached safety, the wounded animal charged toward him. Gray Fox stepped swiftly to one side and the enraged beast, unable to stop, plunged over the cliff to the ledge below.

Gray Fox climbed down the steep rocks. The mountain lion was dead. He skinned the animal and hung the skin to dry. Now there was plenty of food for the eagles.

Mother Eagle Repays Gray Fox

One morning, when Gray Fox awakened on the ledge, the mother eagle was gone. He waited, talking to the young eagles who were now strong and well fed. Soon he saw the mother eagle returning, and in her claws she carried a wild pig. She dropped the prize at the feet of Gray Fox. He knew she was repaying him for his kindness.

Now the golden eagle was well again. She could fly out each day for food to supply the needs of her family. Gray Fox knew his usefulness here had ended. He could rejoin the tribe. But first he pulled a red-gold feather from the tail of the mother eagle.

Gray Fox Joins the Braves

Wearing the lion skin over his shoulder
and the prized feather in his belt, Gray Fox
started the long walk homeward. But as he
neared the end of the journey, he became
filled with doubt about the feather.

"A feather from the tail of the fierce live
eagle," his father had said to him before he
left. By the time he arrived home, he realized that his was not a fierce eagle.

34

Quickly, Gray Fox found his father. He showed him the feather and told his story.

When the story was finished, Big Chief Beaver asked, "But was it you, alone, who killed the mountain lion?"

"No," said Gray Fox, "I only wounded him. He was killed when he plunged over the mountain cliff."

Big Chief Beaver lowered his head and thought for a while. Finally he raised his head and looked at his son. "I will speak with the wise men of the tribe," he said.

The wise men were called together, and Big Chief Beaver spoke. "My son has brought his prize, a tail feather from the mighty golden eagle, and he wears the skin of the fierce mountain lion. He is ready to hunt with the braves, but first you must hear his story."

Again, Gray Fox told his story. He waited eagerly for the wise men's decision. There was a long silence.

Then White Cloud, the oldest Indian, spoke, "You will join the braves. Your trophy was won by skill. You have tamed the fierce golden eagle with your kindness. It takes far greater courage to show kindness to a fierce foe, than to rob him of a tail feather and run from his anger."

The wise Indians nodded their heads in agreement.

Gray Fox treasured the memory of his eagles. But he treasured even more the wise words White Cloud had spoken: "It takes far greater courage to show kindness to a fierce foe."

Trees

Trees are the kindest things I know,
They do no harm, they simply grow
And spread a shade for sleepy cows,
And gather birds among their boughs.
They give us fruit in leaves above,
And wood to make our houses of,
And leaves to burn on Hallowe'en,
And in the Spring new buds of green.
They are the first when day's begun
To touch the beams of morning sun.
They are the last to hold the light
When evening changes into night,
And when a moon floats on the sky
They hum a drowsy lullaby
Of sleeping children long ago . . .
Trees are the kindest things I know.

—Harry Behn

"Trees" from *The Little Hill,* copyright, 1949, by Harry Behn. Reprinted by permission of Harcourt, Brace & World, Inc.

PART 2

We Visit

Bobby Visits a Post Office

A New Puppy

Bobby Jackson was seven years old. He lived on Mulberry Street with his mother and father.

Bobby had always wanted to have a dog. So, when he was seven years old, his mother and father gave him a puppy for his birthday. The puppy was black and white.

40

"What shall we call the new puppy?" asked Father. "Every dog should have a name."

"Let's call him Spot," said Mother. "He has a white spot on his head. Spot would be a good name."

"We could call him Wiggle Waggle," said Bobby. "See how his tail wiggles and waggles all the time?"

"Wiggle Waggle is too long for a dog's name," said Father. "Think how funny you would sound when you called him. You would have to say, 'Here, Wiggle Waggle! Here, Wiggle Waggle!' I think one name would be better. Let's call him Waggles."

They all thought that was a good name, so the new puppy was called Waggles.

Bobby and Waggles played together every day. Bobby taught Waggles how to play tag. Waggles would sit on the porch until Bobby hid behind a tree or bush, or in the garage. Then the puppy would run to find him. When he found Bobby, he would bark and wag his tail as fast as it would go.

Bobby also taught Waggles to sit up by himself, to lie down as though he were sleeping, and to shake hands. The boy and his puppy became very good friends.

But sometimes Bobby thought it was a lot of trouble to have a dog. Waggles would run into the street, and Bobby would have to call him back. And he would dig in the garden and get dirty. Then Bobby would have to wash him. Sometimes Bobby got a little tired of taking care of his dog.

One day something happened that made Bobby decide it was just too much work to take care of a dog. It had rained all morning. The grass was wet, and there were little puddles of water and mud in the garden.

Bobby and Waggles were sitting on the back porch eating a couple of cookies when Bobby's mother came out. She said, "I have just washed the kitchen floor, Bobby. It is sparkling clean. You and Waggles must not come into the kitchen until the floor is dry."

"All right," said Bobby. "We will stay here."

But a few minutes later Bobby found himself in quite a lot of trouble. A little rabbit came hopping across the backyard. Waggles leaped from the porch and chased the bunny into the garden.

He did not catch the bunny. The ground was so soft and wet in the garden that he could not run fast. His feet sank deep into the mud.

By this time Waggles was very excited. He always got excited when he saw a rabbit. He raced back to the porch as fast as he could go, barking and wagging his tail.

Waggles was so excited that he ran right into the kitchen and across the clean floor. His feet left muddy tracks.

When Bobby's mother saw the tracks on her clean floor, she went out to talk to him.

"Just look what your dog did to my clean floor!" she said. "You must wipe up all of the mud from the floor. Then you will have to wash Waggles."

Bobby cleaned the floor and washed the dog. Then he sat on the porch and thought about all the trouble it was to have a dog. "I know what I will do," he said. "I will give Waggles to someone who likes to take care of a dog."

Bobby Writes a Letter

Bobby had a friend named David, who lived in another part of the city. David liked Bobby's dog. Once he told Bobby that he wished he had a dog just like Waggles.

"I will write a letter to David," said Bobby to himself, "and tell him to come and get Waggles if he wants him." Bobby wrote the letter. Here is what it said—

Dear David,

    If you want a bad dog
that is a lot of trouble,
please come and get Wag-
gles. I don't want him
any longer.

                Your friend,

                Bobby

Bobby took the letter to a mailbox on the corner of his street and mailed it. But when he got back home and sat down again on the porch, he began to feel sad. Waggles was clean now and this made him feel good.

47

He wanted to play with Bobby. He sat up
as straight as a stick and held out a paw
to shake hands. Then he licked Bobby's face
as if to say he was sorry about the muddy
floor.

This was enough for Bobby. "I don't
want to give you away," he said to Waggles. "You are a good dog. You are my best
friend. It is no trouble to take care of you.
Let's go to the mailbox and get my letter
back."

Bobby and Waggles went to the mailbox. Bobby tried to look into the box, but it was dark in there. He could not see his letter and, of course, he could not get it out. So he sat down on his wagon and began to think.

"I must find a way to get the letter back," he said. "I must! I must! If I don't get it before it goes to David, I will not have Waggles any more. But how am I going to get it?"

Mr. Miller Explains

Just then a man named Mr. Miller came along the street. He lived next door to Bobby on Mulberry Street. He stopped to talk with Bobby. "Why do you look so sad?" asked Mr. Miller.

When Bobby told Mr. Miller about the letter, Mr. Miller smiled and said, "Why don't you wait until the mail carrier comes to open the box, then ask him how to get the letter?"

"When will the mail carrier come?" asked Bobby.

"Just look on the box here," said Mr. Miller. "It says right on the box when the mail will be picked up."

Bobby and Mr. Miller looked at a sign on the box. It said that mail was taken from the box at 6:15 A.M. and 9:30 A.M. and at 1:30 P.M. and 5:30 P.M.

"What does A.M. and P.M. mean?" asked Bobby.

"A.M. means morning and P.M. means afternoon," said Mr. Miller, "and look at my watch! It says the time is now twenty minutes after one o'clock. That means the mail carrier will be here in ten minutes."

The Mail Carrier

Bobby sat down to wait. Ten minutes later a mail truck stopped at the box and a woman got out. She opened the mailbox with a key and took out many letters. As she was putting them in a mailbag, Bobby went up to her.

"Ms. Mail Carrier," said Bobby, "I wrote a letter and put it in the box. But now I want the letter back. Will you give it to me? It is a green letter and it is going to my friend, David Adams. He lives on Maple Street."

"I am very sorry," said the mail carrier, "but I cannot give you the letter. I cannot be sure that it is your letter. We are not allowed to give back any letters that are put into these boxes because we might give one to a person who should not have it."

"What will I do?" asked Bobby. "Somebody will take my dog unless I get that letter back. Please give it to me."

The mail carrier told Bobby there was a way he might get the letter back. "Go to the post office," she said, "and somebody there will help you."

How a Post Office Works

Bobby ran home to tell his father what had happened. "Will you take me to the post office?" he asked.

Bobby's father took him to the post office and asked to see the Postmaster. The Postmaster was a very friendly man. He took Bobby and his father into his office and asked them to sit down. Then he brought a paper for Bobby's father to fill out.

Bobby's father had to tell on the paper where the letter was mailed and at what time it was put into the mailbox. He also wrote down the size of the letter and what Bobby had written up in the corner of the envelope where the sender puts his return address. Then he wrote the name and address of the boy who was to get the letter.

After Father signed his name at the bottom of the paper, the Postmaster sent for the letter and gave it to Bobby.

Bobby was very happy to get the letter back. He thanked the Postmaster for helping him keep Waggles.

"While you are here, Bobby," said the Postmaster, "would you like to see how a post office is operated and how your letters are handled?"

"I would," said Bobby. "That would be interesting."

The Postmaster took Bobby and his father out to the parking lot first. That is where the mail trucks bring in the mail from all parts of town. They saw how the bags of letters are taken from the trucks to a sorting room. In this room some men open the bags, take out all of the mail, and lay it on tables.

The letters then go through a machine that cancels the stamps so they cannot be used again and tells which post office the letters come from. Then each letter is put in a box that has printed on it the name of the city to which the letter is going.

All of the letters that go to one place are then put in a bag with the name of that place on it. The bags are then taken, either in trucks or on trains, to those places. Letters that have airmail stamps on them are carried in airplanes.

When a letter gets to the city or town where it should go, it is placed in the box of a certain mail carrier at the post office and he delivers it to the right house.

Bobby and his father enjoyed their trip to the post office. When they got home, Bobby hugged Waggles and said to him, "Good old Waggles. The Postmaster is a fine friend to have."

Visit to a Library — *clues*

▶ *Introduction* Planning a Trip — *clues*

Susan Davidson lived in a town called West Bend. She was in second grade at the West Bend Elementary School. Susan and her friend, Sally Green, walked to school together each day.

clues

One morning Miss White, their teacher, asked the class if they would like to visit one of the large buildings in town before school closed for the year.

"Oh, yes!" cried the class. "What building will we visit?"

58

Larry Johnson raised his hand. "How about going to the library?" he asked. "If we knew how the library works, then maybe we could join it."

"A good suggestion," replied the teacher. "And if you join the library, perhaps you will find time to read some books during the summer vacation. We will go to the library some day next week."

Susan and Sally were excited about the trip. They ran all the way home from school that day. As Susan hurried into her house, she called, "Mother! Mother! Guess what! Miss White is taking us to visit the library. We are going on a bus, and we plan to eat our lunch in the park. What fun we will have!"

Each day the class talked about the trip they were going to take. Sally and Susan talked about it on their way to and from school.

"I am going to wear my new blue dress," said Sally.

"I have a new sweater I can wear," Susan said.

The Bus Ride

At last the day for the trip came. The sun was shining brightly, and the school bus was parked in front of the school.

Everyone came to school all dressed up. The girls wore ribbons in their hair, and almost every boy wore a necktie.

"My," said Miss White, "how nice you all look for our trip today."

Then all of the boys and girls in the second grade class went out and got into the bus.

Sally and Susan sat in the first seat, just behind the bus driver. When everyone was seated, the bus started down the street. It went past the house where Susan lived, past the post office and the park, where they would eat their lunches. At last the bus came to the library.

Can their be clues

The Librarian Explains

"Who is that on the library steps?" asked Sally.

"That is the librarian," said Miss White. "She is expecting us. She will take us through the library and explain things to us."

So Ms. White don't

The bus stopped. The children went up to the steps where the librarian greeted them. "Good morning, children," she said. "How nice of you to visit our library. Before we go inside, I want to explain to you that everyone must be quiet in a library. We do not want to disturb people who are reading or studying."

62

do all the talk!

"Now, when we first go into the building, we will go to a room where I can explain how our library works. You may talk and ask questions there. But when we go through the rooms where people are reading, you must be quiet."

So, two by two, the class went around the building and into a room. It looked almost like a classroom at school. The children sat on little chairs in rows. The librarian stood up front, just as Miss White did at school. She started to explain to the children. "First," she said, "a person must join the library to be able to take a book home to read." She held a card up for the pupils to see. "This little card has a place where you write how old you are."

librarian

"May we join?" asked Sally.

"Yes," said the librarian, "if your mother
or father will sign a card for you, we will
be glad to have you join our library. I will
give a card to each of you before you leave.
When you return it, after your mother or
father has signed it, we will give you a card
like this." And she held up a smaller card
for the class to see.

"When you take a book from our library, we stamp a date on a slip that is pasted inside the back cover of the book. That is the date when the book should be returned, and it is always there in the book for you to check on it. If you keep a book until after the date stamped on that slip, you are charged one cent for each day it is kept overdue. At the same time we take a photograph of your library card beside a card that shows the title of the book. This gives us a record of who has the book out. Some libraries have you just show your card and sign your name on the card that has the title of the book on it."

The librarian then held up some other cards and a drawer. She said, "I will tell you about the card catalogue that helps you find a certain book. We look in this drawer for the card that has the name of the book on it. This card has a number on it. That number tells us the section of the library where the book may be found."

"When we go to the children's department, I will show you the card catalogue
that you may use when you belong to the
library. But, now, let's go on down to the
library hospital."

"The what?" asked Larry, with a puzzled
look on his face.

The librarian smiled. She said, "The library hospital is the room where torn and
damaged books are mended."

Two by two, the children got into a line
again and followed the librarian down a
long hall. Sally and Susan led the class.

Squeak, Squeak

Everyone tried to be quiet. But with every other step you could hear a loud squeaking noise.

"Sh-h-h-h!" said Miss White. "We must be quiet." But the noise did not stop.

The librarian stopped and looked around. "Shhh!" she said.

The whole class stopped in front of the librarian—and the noise stopped too.

Then the librarian, Miss White, and the class started once more down the hall. And the noise began again. "Squeak, squeak" went the noise, louder than before.

The librarian led the children into a room where two women were working. They were mending pages that had been torn and erasing pencil marks. And if the cover of a book were damaged, they rebound the book. That means they made a new cover for it.

"Now you see, children," said the librarian, "why we call this the library hospital. Here we try to make old books look almost like new again."

Then the librarian started down another hall. The children all followed. And the squeaking noise followed too.

68

"Sounds like a mouse squeaking," whispered Sally. Susan giggled, and the noise kept on.

Once again the librarian stopped the class. "Shhh!" she said. When the class stopped, the squeaks stopped. When the class started up again, so did the noise.

"Shhh!" said Sally. "Shhh!" said Susan. Soon almost every one of the children was saying, "Shhh." Then they all began to laugh, for by this time the children were making so much noise saying "Shh!" that nobody could hear the squeaking sound.

When everybody was quiet again, the librarian took the class into the adult section. And into the adult section went the squeaking noise.

Some men and women were sitting at tables reading books. Some of them looked up when they heard the squeaking noise.

The children looked up and down the rows and rows of shelves. The shelves were almost as high as the ceiling, and they were filled with books.

"Squeak, squeak," went the squeaking noise, as the pupils walked around. "Shh! Shh!" said Susan. "Shh! Shh!" said Sally. But the noise kept right on.

The librarian and Miss White hurried the class on to the children's department.

"These are the drawers full of cards that I told you about," said the librarian, "and the shelves are numbered in sections. Each card tells where to find a certain book on the shelves. Now I will give you the kind of card that you may take home. When you and your father or mother have filled it out and you bring it back, you may begin to take books home. You may look around now for books you might like to take out."

The children tiptoed from shelf to shelf, looking at the many books. And the squeaking noise started up again.

Susan Finds the Noise

"Shh!" whispered Susan. And all the class stood still. That is, everyone stood still except Larry Johnson. He was walking along, looking at a shelf filled with stories of adventure. And as Larry walked there was a squeak with every step.

All of the children laughed. "Larry made the squeaking noise," said Susan. "He made the noise with his new shoes."

Larry looked down at his shoes. "I am sorry I made such a noise," he said. "Next time I come to the library I will not wear squeaky shoes."

After the class left the library, they went to the park to eat their lunches. Then they ran and played and laughed until Miss White said it was time to go home.

Everybody had a good time and learned how to get books from the library.

A Trip to the City

David Wilson was ten years old and had
lived all his life in the city. He lived on the
eighth floor of a tall apartment building.
It was summer, and David had invited his
cousin George for a week's vacation. George
had never been to the city before. He lived
on a farm in the middle of the state.

At last the day came when George was
to arrive. George felt quite grown up coming
alone by train to the city for a visit. But
he was glad to see David and his father
when the train pulled into the station.
Everything looked very strange.

Ride on a Subway

"Let's take the subway home," said David.

"What's a subway?" asked George.

"It's something like the train you came on, George," said David's father. "But it's an electric train and it goes underground. Yes, we can take the subway home."

"Why underground?" asked George.

"To save time," replied David's father. "You do not have to cross streets and wait for traffic lights. And no cars or people can get in your way. By taking a subway a person can get from one side of the city across to the other side in a short time."

So Father, George, and David went through the gate to the subway. George's eyes got as big as saucers because the subway zoomed away underground.

They left the subway at the station nearest David's home. As they walked along the block, George was chattering excitedly about the subway when Father said, "Well, we're home."

Forty-Eight Little Houses

George gulped and looked up at the tall building. "You mean you live here? This house reaches almost to the sky."

"Not quite to the sky, George," laughed David's father. "Yes, we live here. We have an apartment on the eighth floor. The building is twelve stories high, and there are four apartments on each floor."

"You mean forty-eight different families all live here?" asked George.

"Yes," replied David's father, "and each family has its own separate apartment. Just like forty-eight little houses all under one big roof."

"Oh," said George shaking his head in amazement as he followed David and his father into the building. He was still thinking about the forty-eight little houses all under one big roof when he followed David and his father into the elevator.

David's father pressed a button and the door of the elevator closed.

"We're in a cage!" shouted George. "How do we get out?"

"Don't be frightened, George," said David's father. "We're in an elevator, and it will take us to the floor we live on."

"You see, George," said David, "this saves us from walking up all those steps to the eighth floor."

David's mother met them at the door of the apartment. "Come in, George," she said. "You must be hungry after your long trip. Dinner will be ready in a little while."

David showed George his room and some of his new toys and games. But George was more interested in looking out of the window and watching all the new things he saw in the city.

"Look, David," called George, "the people walking on the sidewalk look no taller than dolls."

David laughed. "That's because we're up so high," he said.

Just then a siren blew, and a fire engine came racing around the corner. A few minutes later a second engine followed the first with its sirens blaring. What a racket it made! George held his hands over his ears as he shouted to David, "We don't have this much noise in the country."

After dinner George and David played games and talked until time for bed. George was tired, but he could not fall asleep right away. He was not used to all the noise there was in the city. He heard cars going by on the street below, and he could hear people laughing and talking. And he saw the bright lights of signs flashing off and on in the distance.

Big Stores

During the next few days George was excited by all the different things he saw in the city. He even went to one of the big supermarkets. He pushed the cart for David's mother as she gathered things from the shelves to place in the cart. "How different," said George to himself. "At home we don't have to buy so many things to eat at a store because we grow them in a garden."

One morning, near the end of the week, David's mother called to the boys, "Come on, sleepyheads, time to get up! Father left for work an hour ago, and I think today we will visit one of the department stores."

After the boys had had breakfast and were all dressed and ready to go, David's mother said, "Since George has never been in one, we'll take a taxicab to the store."

George watched the meter in the taxicab as they drove to the department store. David's mother had told George that that was the machine that told the driver how much money to ask for at the end of the ride. David pointed out some of the places he had been to as they drove by. "I've been there with Father," he said, as they passed the zoo and the museum.

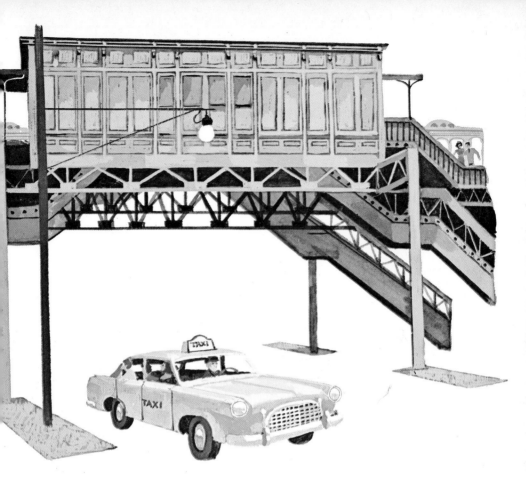

David's mother pointed to the elevated train as it went by. "See, George," she said. "By taking the elevated train one can get across the city in a short time without having to stop for other cars or people."

"Just like the subway," said David.

"I never thought I would see a train in the air or under the ground," said George. And he had such a serious look on his face that David and his mother both laughed.

By this time the taxicab had stopped in front of the department store. David's mother paid the driver; then she and the boys went into the store. As they went from one department to another, George shook his head and said to himself, "I never knew they made such big stores where you could buy just about anything."

"Here's that cage again!" said George as David's mother took the boys on the elevator. She was taking them up to the toy department so they could look around.

A large display of electric trains caught George's eye. "Just what I should like to have," he thought to himself. A man was showing the boys how the train went around the different tracks and through tunnels and how the engine even whistled just like a real one. The boys kept watching the trains until David's mother called to them to come because she had some shopping to do.

So the boys left the train display and followed David's mother to another department. But George kept glancing back toward the train display. David's mother stopped then and was looking at some things to buy and talking to David.

Lost and Found

"I'll just go back and watch the trains, while they are standing here," thought George to himself. "Then when they are ready to go to another department, I'll be ready to go with them."

So back to the train display went George. Every few minutes he would glance around and still see David and his mother.

All at once he looked and he couldn't see them at all. George walked toward the department where he thought they were. No, they were not there. So he walked on to another department. Still he did not see them. George was lost!

By this time David and his mother realized that George was not with them. "I think he went back to the trains," said David. So back to the trains they went. But George was not at the trains now.

"We must find George," said David's mother. "He isn't used to the city, and he will be frightened." They looked and looked, but when they looked in one department George was in another department.

George kept searching and searching for David and his mother, but by now he was very confused. He didn't even remember where the train display was.

"What will I do?" said George to himself. "If I don't find them by dinner time, how will I eat?" And George kept on walking from one department to another.

The store was getting very crowded now. There were so many big people that George couldn't see over their heads, but he just kept on walking. George felt tears coming to his eyes. He brushed them away with his hand.

George had followed along with the crowd until he came to some steps. The other people started up the steps, but George just stood and watched. It seemed to him that after the people got on the steps they just stood still and the steps moved.

"I must be dreaming," said George, and he pinched himself to see whether he was.

He watched the people on the steps until the steps just seemed to disappear while the people kept right on moving out of sight.

George watched for a while; and then he started walking again, looking for David and his mother. "If I can't find them, where will I sleep tonight?" asked George. As he said this he was going through the women's coat department. "I guess I could sleep on one of those coats," he said to himself.

David's mother was searching everywhere for George. She asked the man at the train display if he had seen George. She asked the store manager. But no one had seen George.

George had walked and walked and walked through one department after another and from one floor to another. He was tired and hungry, and although eight-year-old boys don't cry, George could feel the tears coming down his cheeks.

A kind man saw him and asked, "What's the matter, young man?"

"I can't find my cousin or his mother," said George.

"What is your cousin's last name?" asked the man.

"Wilson," said George. "My cousin's name is David Wilson."

"Come with me; we'll find them," said the man. So he took George up to the office of the store manager, and he spoke into a loud speaker. "Would Mrs. Wilson please come to the manager's office," he said.

David and his mother heard the voice over the loud speaker and rushed up to the office. George was very happy to see David and his mother. And they were happy to see George too. "I was worried about you, George," said David's mother.

While eating dinner that evening, George told David and David's mother and father about the moving steps in the department store and how they disappeared.

"That's an escalator," cried David.

David's father smiled as he explained, "An escalator is a stairway arranged like an endless belt, so that the steps go up or down all the time."

"I never thought I would see steps that move," said George, laughing with David. "In fact," he said, "I never thought I would see many of the things I have seen here in the city. This has been a fine vacation."

The Park

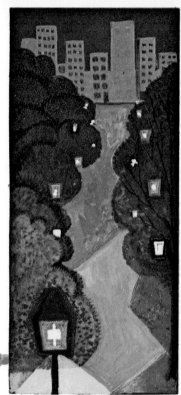

I'm glad that I
   Live near a park
For in the winter
   After dark
The park lights shine
   As bright and still
As dandelions
   On a hill.

—*James S. Tippett*

The Wind Has Many Faces

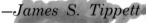

The wind has many faces
Which we can never see;
A spring face filled with lilacs,
A face of salt, foam sea;
An angry, purple storm face,
A white face iced in snow,
And when we think they're all asleep,
Another starts to blow!

—*Adele H. Seronde*

93

Shore

Play on the seashore
And gather up shells,
Kneel in the damp sands
Digging wells.

Run on the rocks
Where the seaweed slips,
Watch the waves
And the beautiful ships.

—*Mary Britton Miller*

PART 3

Fun With Animals

A Strange Friend

Mr. Hickey Hears Something

Mr. Hickey was quite an old man. He lived in a little cabin he had built for himself on an island. The island was in the ocean near the state of Florida.

There were many animals on this island. They lived among the thick bushes and trees. In the water around the land there were several kinds of fish. Mr. Hickey had a fishing boat and he went fishing almost every day. He ate some of the fish but sold most of them so that he could buy other things to eat.

"A Strange Friend" from *The Phantom Deer*, by Joseph Wharton Lippincott. Copyright 1954 by Joseph Wharton Lippincott. Published by J. B. Lippincott Company.

One night Mr. Hickey was sitting at his table, writing a letter. The only light in the cabin came from two small candles, one on each side of him. Outside, a low new moon was trying to shine on the water, and stars were twinkling.

At a moment when all was quiet except for the croaking of frogs, the old man heard a strange sound. He listened carefully. Minutes passed, then he heard it again.

"I had better have a look," he thought. He rose slowly, picked up a flashlight from among his tools on a side table, and silently moved to the closed door. Then he swung the door open quickly and flashed the light into the woods.

At first, he saw only bushes. He moved the beam of light slowly to the left, then to the right. Here he saw two large eyes gleaming in the light. Without winking, the eyes stared at him. He stared back, frightened and wondering what great animal might be ready to pounce upon him. The bushes were high and thick at this spot near the cabin. They hid all but the large eyes.

"That animal is only two good jumps away!" thought Mr. Hickey. "It might be a panther or a bear or something I've never seen before, maybe from a circus." He moved back into the room and looked for something he could use to help save himself from the danger. The handle of an axe caught his eye and he grasped it.

"No animal can lick me now!" he said.

When he stepped out again and flashed the light, the eyes were still there, glowing and not moving, but just a little closer. Mr. Hickey hesitated, peering carefully into the shadows, trying to make out the hidden form. Then he took a step toward it, the axe handle gripped in his big right hand.

He moved softly, his feet feeling their way among the stiff growing things in their path.

Suddenly he stopped. In the thin glare of the light he saw a spotted animal not much larger than a small dog. A fawn was standing there, its ears standing up and its large eyes staring at him in helpless fear.

The Baby Deer

Mr. Hickey laughed to himself. He didn't want to spend time looking at another deer. He saw some nearly every day on his island. Their dainty tracks were everywhere. Slowly he lowered the axe handle, took one more look at the tiny animal, then turned around and started back toward his cabin.

But he was not to get rid of the baby deer that easily. When he reached his doorway, he found the little animal at his heels. It was following him, almost nudging his legs.

Mr. Hickey stamped one foot at the fawn but it did not run away. It stood there looking at him, propped up on wide-apart, shaky legs.

"I wonder where its mother is," thought Mr. Hickey. "It must be lost, or sick maybe, or just crazy."

He stepped into the room. The fawn stayed in the doorway because it was afraid to place its little hoofs on the board floor. The man stooped and put an arm around it, gently pulling it into the room. The little thing's hoofs slipped on the smooth boards and it fell toward him, trying hard to get on its feet. But it could not; so it just lay there panting.

The old man's heart warmed toward the little animal. He got down on his hands and knees and examined it. It seemed to be nearly all legs.

Mr. Hickey closed the door, set one of the candles on the floor nearby, and flashed his light around the room. On a shelf he saw three cans of milk. Quickly he took one of the cans and punched two holes in its top. Then he poured some of the milk and a little water into a bowl and placed it under the nose of the fawn. The little deer did not seem interested in the bowl but grasped the man's thumb in its mouth and sucked on it.

The old man understood what the deer wanted, so he lowered his thumb into the bowl and gently pushed the fawn's mouth into the milk. Still holding hard to the thumb, the dainty little animal sucked and sucked, and soon the milk was gone.

After the fawn had another bowlful of milk, it walked gingerly around the room, then lay down close to Mr. Hickey's chair.

That night Mr. Hickey slept on his narrow cot in one end of the cabin. The fawn slept on the floor beside him on an old coat.

The next morning, when the old man was eating his breakfast, the fawn walked around and around his chair and silently watched him eat.

After feeding the fawn, Mr. Hickey opened the door, stepped out, and took a look at the water and his boat. He was getting ready to go fishing. The fawn followed him.

"Say, you!" warned the man. "This won't do. Go back inside before some big animal gets you. I'll be home in time to feed you again." He gently pushed the soft little fellow into the cabin and closed the door, wishing he had not looked at the hurt in its eyes.

"That deer is going to be a big bother," thought the old man. "Seems to love me like a mother. Well, I've got to catch fish if I am going to buy food for it too." He started toward the boat, then turned around and tiptoed to the window. He saw the fawn standing sadly beside his chair.

"That animal is getting me down," he mumbled. "I feel mean all over leaving him here alone."

The old man went on with his fishing trip. By noon he had caught thirty snappers. Then he went in his boat to a landing where there was a store. The store was operated by a man named Shorty.

After Mr. Hickey sold his fish, he bought twelve cans of milk.

"What are you going to do with all of the milk?" asked Shorty. "You must have a baby at the house," he laughed.

"Yes, I do have a baby," said Mr. Hickey. Shorty took this as a great joke and laughed loudly.

"Boy or girl?"

"Boy," said Hickey, "of course."

"Well, bring him around sometime!" laughed Shorty. "That I want to see!"

"Were there any accidents on the road yesterday?" asked the old man. "Did anyone run into a deer?"

"Well, there was a deer run over two nights ago," said Shorty. "Nobody hurt, though."

"That must have been the little fawn's mother," thought the old man to himself.

All the way to his boat he was thinking about the motherless fawn. "I must not tell anybody too much about anything these days," he said to himself. "They might take the little fellow away from me."

When Mr. Hickey got near his home, he called out to the closed door, "Hi, little fellow!" A soft bleat greeted him. When he swung the door open, the fawn ran to meet him and jumped up and down around his legs.

"My, you are frisky," he said happily. "You're going to be all right!" He picked up the little animal and stroked its soft ears. "How about some milk?"

This time the fawn kept on sucking up the milk after he took away his thumb.

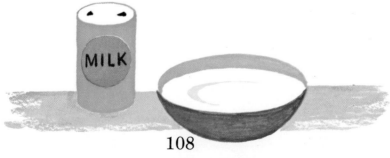

The Fawn Grows Up

After that, each day was the same as the one before, except that the fawn grew stouter and friskier. Mr. Hickey no longer tried to make it stay indoors, and sometimes he even took it with him in his boat. It learned to run fast and jump over bushes higher than its head.

One morning when Mr. Hickey was getting ready to go fishing, he called to the fawn, "Come along, you! Let's see if we can catch some fish today." The deer jumped into the boat and off they went. But the fish were not easily caught that day; so the old man kept on going farther and farther around the island.

When the boat was about three miles from home, suddenly the fawn jumped into the water and began racing toward the shore. He had seen two older deer there and wanted to be with them.

"I guess that is the last I will see of my friend," said the old man to himself. "When a deer grows up, it wants to be with other deer. I have seen the fawn looking at those two deer before. I suppose they have been calling to him in their own way."

The old man did see his pet deer again. Sometimes he would see him racing through the woods or just standing still, looking at his old friend. The deer grew big and strong and had fine antlers.

He became a great fighter. In fact, he and another young buck deer became the two best fighters on the island. Together, they fought all of the other bucks, but they never fought with each other. They were so much alike that they were called twins.

Once, during the deer-hunting season, the two bucks almost got killed. They were running together when three hunters came into the woods. The hunters had dogs. Suddenly the dogs sniffed the air and knew there were some deer in the woods. They started after them, barking loudly.

The deer ran as fast as they could, but the dogs were able to follow them because they could smell their tracks.

The dogs chased the deer all afternoon. When evening came, the dogs were so tired they could not run much farther. The twin bucks were tired too. It was then that the bucks waded into the shallow water of a small lake and waited for the pack of dogs.

The dogs plunged into the water, straight for the two bucks, that stood side by side. Suddenly Hickey's buck charged at one of the dogs, catching him under the chin and throwing him backward. Before the deer could move back, another dog was up to him and about to spring upon him. But the other buck jumped at him, catching him in the chest with his antlers.

There were three dogs and only two deer. It began to look as though the deer would lose the fight if it lasted very long. But the deer fought on. They stood side by side and fought with their antlers and their sharp hoofs.

Before very long, the dogs knew they were beaten, and they went away. The two bucks then hurried to safety.

Two days later, Mr. Hickey saw his pet deer in the woods. The deer came up close to him and the old man knew it was his friend. This worried Mr. Hickey. The deer was too friendly for his own good. He might go too near to a hunter. Mr. Hickey stamped his feet and screamed at the deer. The buck raced away into the woods. "My pet deer will not understand why his old friend screamed at him," said Mr. Hickey, "but he must learn not to trust people he meets in the woods."

Henry and Ribs

Henry Huggins was in the third grade at school. His hair looked like a scrubbing brush and most of his grown-up front teeth were in. He lived with his mother and father in a square white house on Klickitat Street. Except for having his tonsils out when he was six and breaking his arm falling out of a cherry tree when he was seven, nothing much happened to Henry.

"I wish something exciting would happen," Henry often thought.

But nothing very interesting ever happened to Henry, at least not until one Saturday afternoon in March.

Every Saturday afternoon Henry rode downtown on the bus to go swimming at the Y.M.C.A. After he had swum for an hour, he got on the bus again and rode home just in time for dinner.

When Henry left the Y.M.C.A. on this particular Saturday, he had four dimes and a nickel in his pocket. So he went to the corner drugstore to buy a chocolate ice-cream cone. He thought he would eat the ice-cream cone, get on the bus, drop twenty-five cents in the slot, and ride home.

That is not what happened.

Henry Finds a Friend

He bought the ice-cream cone with one of his dimes. Then, as he was standing outside of the drugstore licking his chocolate ice-cream cone, he heard a thump, thump, thump.

Henry turned, and there behind him was a dog. He wasn't any special kind of dog. He was too small to be a big dog, but, on the other hand, he was much too big to be a little dog. He wasn't a white dog because where he was not white, there were little patches of brown. And in between there were black and yellow spots.

The dog was hungry. When Henry licked, he licked. When Henry swallowed, he swallowed.

"Hello, you old dog," Henry said. "You can't have my ice-cream cone."

Swish, swish, swish went the dog's tail back and forth. "Just one bite," his brown eyes seemed to say.

"Go away," said Henry. But he wasn't very firm about it. He patted the dog's head. The tail wagged harder. Henry took one last lick. "Oh, all right," he said. "If you are that hungry, you might as well have it."

The ice-cream cone disappeared down the dog's throat in one gulp.

"Now go away," Henry told the dog. "I have to catch a bus for home."

He started to walk. The dog started, too.

"Go away, you skinny old dog." Henry didn't say it very loudly. "Go on home."

The dog sat down at Henry's feet. Henry looked at the dog and the dog looked at Henry.

"I don't think you have a home," said Henry. "You are awful thin. Your ribs show right through your skin."

Thump, thump, thump replied the dog's tail.

"And you haven't got a collar," said Henry.

A Telephone Call to Mother

Henry began to think. If only he could keep the dog! He had always wanted a dog of his very own, and now he had found a dog that wanted him. He couldn't go home and leave a hungry dog on the street corner. If only he knew what his mother and father would say! He fingered the dimes in his pocket. That was it! He would use one of the dimes to phone his mother.

"Come on, Ribsy. Come on, Ribs, old boy. I'm going to call you Ribs because you're so thin."

The dog trotted after the boy to the telephone booth in the corner of the drugstore. Henry shoved him into the booth and shut the door. He had never used a pay telephone before. He had to put the telephone book on the floor and stand on tiptoe on it to reach the coin box. He put a dime into the coin box and gave the operator his number.

"Hello—Mom?"

"Why, Henry!" His mother sounded surprised. "Where are you?"

"At the drugstore near the Y."

Ribs began to scratch. Thump, thump, thump. Inside the telephone booth the thumps sounded loud and hollow.

"For goodness' sake, Henry, what's the noise?" his mother asked. Ribs began to whimper and then to howl. "Henry," Mrs. Huggins shouted, "are you all right?"

"Yes, I'm all right. That's just Ribsy."

"Ribsy?" His mother was very surprised. "Henry," she said, "who is Ribsy? Will you please tell me what is going on?"

"I'm trying to," said Henry. Ribsy howled louder. "Mother, I've found a dog. I wish I could keep him. He's a good dog and I'd feed him and wash him and everything. Please, Mom."

"I don't know, dear," his mother said. "You'll have to ask your father."

"Mom!" Henry wailed. "That's what you always say!" Henry was tired of standing on tiptoe, and the phone booth was getting warm. "Mom, please say yes, and I'll never ask you for another thing as long as I live!"

"Well, all right, Henry. I guess there isn't any reason why you shouldn't have a dog. But you will have to bring him home on the bus. Your father has the car today and I can't come after you. Can you do that?"

"Sure! Easy," said Henry.

"And, Henry, please don't be late. It looks as if it might rain."

"All right, Mom."

Thump, thump, thump.

"Henry, what's that thumping noise?"

"It's my dog, Ribsy. He's scratching a flea."

"Oh, Henry," Mrs. Huggins moaned. "Couldn't you have found a dog without fleas?"

Henry thought that was a good time to hang up the phone. "Come on, Ribs," he said. "We're going home on the bus."

No Dogs Allowed

When the big green bus stopped in front of the drugstore, Henry picked up his dog. Ribsy was heavy. Henry had a hard time getting him on the bus. Then the bus driver said, "Say, Sonny, you can't take that dog on the bus."

"Why not?" asked Henry.

"It's a company rule. No dogs on buses."

"Golly, Mister, how am I going to get him home?"

"Sorry, Sonny. I didn't make the rule. No animal can ride on a bus unless it's inside a box or unless it's a seeing eye dog."

"Well, thanks anyway," said Henry as he lifted Ribsy off the bus.

"I guess we will have to get you a box," Henry told his dog. "I'll get you on the next bus somehow."

He went back into the drugstore, followed closely by Ribsy. "Have you got a big box I could have, please?" he asked the man at the toothpaste counter. "I need one big enough for my dog."

The clerk leaned over the counter to look at Ribsy. "A cardboard box?" he asked.

"Yes, please," said Henry, wishing the man would hurry. He didn't want to be late getting home.

The clerk pulled the box out from under the counter. "This hair-tonic box is the only one I have. I guess it's big enough, but why anyone would want to put a dog in a cardboard box I can't understand," he said.

The box was about two feet square and six inches deep. On one end was printed, "Don't Let Them Call You Baldy," and on the other, "Try Our Large Economy Size."

Henry thanked the clerk, carried the box out to the bus stop, and put it on the sidewalk. Ribsy paddled after him. "Get in, fellow," Henry commanded. Ribsy understood. He stepped into the box and sat down just as the bus came around the corner.

As Henry lifted the box, Ribsy lovingly licked his face with his wet pink tongue.

The bus stopped at the curb. Henry stepped up into the bus. He asked the driver. "Will you please take the money out of my pocket? My hands are full."

The driver pushed his cap back on his head and exclaimed, "Full! I should say they are full! And just where do you think you're going with that animal?"

"Home," said Henry, in a very small voice.

"Not on this bus, you're not!" said the driver.

"But the man on the last bus said I could take the dog on the bus in a box," said Henry. "He said it was a company rule."

"He meant a big box tied shut. A box with holes punched in it for the dog to breathe through."

Just then Ribsy growled. "Shut up!" said Henry.

Ribsy began to scratch his left ear with his left hind foot. The box began to tear. Ribsy jumped out of the box and off the bus, and Henry jumped after him. The bus pulled away.

"Now see what you've done!" said Henry. "You've spoiled everything." The dog hung his head and tucked his tail between his legs. "If I can't get you home, how can I keep you?" Henry asked the dog.

All at once, Henry had an idea. He ran back into the drugstore and said to the clerk, "May I have one of those big shopping bags?"

Henry opened the bag and shoved Ribsy into it, hind feet first. Then he pushed his front feet in. A lot of Ribsy was left over at the top of the bag.

"I guess I'll have to have some string and paper, too," Henry said to the clerk.

The clerk gave it to him. Ribsy whimpered, but he held still while Henry wrapped the paper loosely around his head and shoulders and tied it with a string.

Ribsy wiggled and whined, even though Henry tried to pet him through the paper. When the bus stopped, Henry climbed on. He dropped his money in the slot and squirmed through the crowd to a seat beside a fat man near the back of the bus.

The driver was the same one he had met on the first bus! But Ribs was on the bus at last. Now if Henry could only keep him quiet for fifteen minutes they would be home and Ribsy would be his.

Trouble on the Bus

Ribsy was quiet for a while. Then he began to whimper and howl. Crackle, crackle, crackle. Thump, thump, thump went the paper bag as Ribsy scratched his way out.

"Well," exclaimed the fat man, as he began to laugh, "if it wasn't a skinny old dog in that bag."

"He is not," said Henry. "He's a good dog."

Henry tried to keep Ribsy between his knees. The bus lurched around a corner and started to go uphill. Henry was thrown against the fat man. The frightened dog wiggled away from him, squirmed between the passengers, and started for the front of the bus.

"Here, Ribsy, old boy! Come back here,"
called Henry, as he started after the dog.

"E-e-ek! A dog!" squealed a lady with a
bag of apples. "Go away, doggie, go away!"

Ribsy was scared. He tried to run and
crashed into the lady's bag of apples. The
bag tipped over and the apples began to
roll toward the back of the bus, which was
grinding up a steep hill. The apples rolled
around the feet of people who were standing. Passengers began to slip and slide.
They dropped their packages and grabbed
one another.

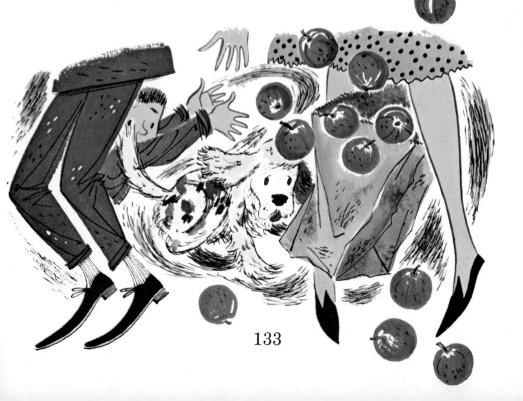

Crash! A girl dropped an armload of books. Rattle! Bang! Crash! A lady dropped a big paper bag. The bag broke open and pots and pans rolled out.

Thud! A man dropped a roll of garden hose. The hose unrolled and the passengers found it wound around their legs.

People were sitting on the floor. They were sitting on books and apples. They were even sitting on other people's laps. Some of them had their hats over their faces and their feet in the air.

Skree-e-etch! The driver threw on the brakes. Then he saw Henry making his way through the apples and the books and pans and hose to catch Ribsy.

The driver pushed his cap back on his head. "Now, Sonny," he said to Henry. "Now you know why dogs are not allowed on buses!"

"Yes, sir," said Henry in a very small voice. "I'm sorry."

The fat man began to snicker. Then he chuckled. Then he laughed and then he roared. He laughed until tears streamed down his cheeks. All of the other passengers were laughing too, even the man with the hose and the lady with the apples.

The driver didn't laugh. "Take that dog and get off the bus," he ordered. Ribsy whimpered and tucked his tail between his legs.

The fat man stopped laughing. "See here, driver," he said, "you can't put that boy and his dog off in the rain."

"Well, he can't stay on the bus," snapped the driver.

Henry didn't know what he was going to do. He guessed he would have to walk the rest of the way in the dark and the rain.

Policemen Come to the Rescue

Just then a siren screamed. It grew louder and louder until it stopped right beside the bus.

A policeman appeared in the bus entrance. "Is there a boy called Henry Huggins on this bus?" he asked.

"I'm him," said Henry in a very small voice.

"Don't say 'I'm him,'" said the lady with the apples, who had been a schoolteacher. "You should say, 'I am he.'"

"You better come along with us," said the policeman.

Henry and Ribsy followed the policeman off the bus and into the squad car, where Henry and the dog sat in the back seat.

"Are you going to arrest me?" Henry asked timidly.

"Well, I don't know," said a policeman. "Do you think you ought to be arrested?"

"No, sir," said Henry politely. He thought the policeman was joking, but he wasn't sure. It was hard to tell about grown-ups sometimes. "I didn't mean to do anything," said Henry. "I just had to get Ribsy home. My mother said I could keep him if I could bring him home on the bus."

"What do you think?" the policeman asked another officer who was driving the car.

"We-e-ell, I think we might let him off this time," answered the driver. "His mother must be pretty worried about him if she called the police, and I don't think she would want him to go to jail."

"Yes, he's late for his dinner already," said the other officer. "Let's see how fast we can get him home."

The driver pushed a button and the siren began to shriek. Ribsy raised his head and howled.

Henry began to enjoy himself. Wouldn't this be something to tell the boys and girls at school. The tires screeched, and people stopped to look as the police car sped up the street.

It turned in on Klickitat Street and stopped in front of Henry's house. Henry's mother and father were standing on the porch. The neighbors were looking out of their windows.

"Well," said Henry's father, after the policemen had gone. "It's about time you came home. So this is Ribsy! I've heard about you, Ribsy, and there is a big bone and a can of flea flakes waiting for you."

"Henry, what will you get into next?" sighed his mother.

"Golly, Mom, I didn't do anything. I just brought my dog home on the bus the way you said."

Ribsy sat down and began to scratch.

The Hairy Dog

My dog's so furry I've not seen
His face for years and years:
His eyes are buried out of sight,
I only guess his ears.

When people ask me for his breed,
I do not know or care:
He has the beauty of them all
Hidden beneath his hair.

—*Herbert Asquith*

The Night Rain

Slowly,
  Coming softly,
    the cool, clean rain
    running down
      down
    with the wind
      through the tree leaves
    stopped to
    talk to
    the night windows. . . .

And then took time
    to sing. . . .
    to sing until
    little
      children
    went to sleep.

—Ellen Trafford

PART 4

Learning to Work and Play

The Centerville Panthers

Jimmy Osgood lived in a town called Centerville. It was not a very big town. There was only one elementary school in Centerville.

Not very far from Centerville there was another small town. The name of it was Brady. There was only one elementary school in Brady, too.

Each of the schools had a baseball team. One was called the Brady Tigers and the other, the Centerville Panthers.

144

In the spring and fall, these two teams played several games with each other. Sometimes the Tigers won and sometimes the Panthers would win.

The Centerville Panthers played their games in a beautiful little park behind the school. It had been built by the people who live in Centerville. It had a swimming pool, swings and slides, and a baseball field.

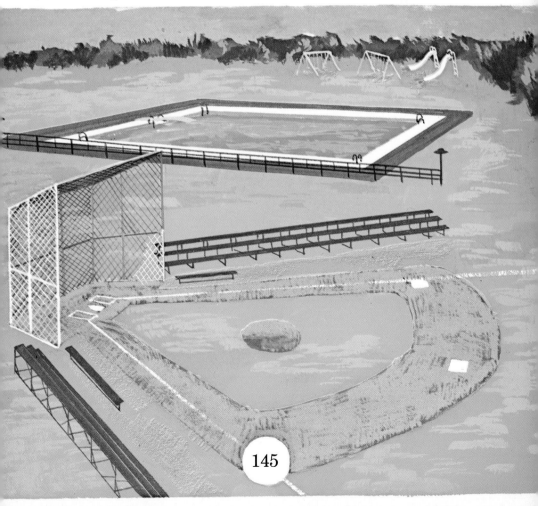

The baseball field had several rows of seats on both sides of it. Centerville people sat on one side, and people who came with the visiting team sat on the other side.

When the Brady Tigers came to play at Centerville, all of the seats were filled. The games were usually very close ones, and many people came to cheer for each team.

Not Big Enough

Most of the players on these teams were between ten and twelve years old. Jimmy Osgood had always wanted to play baseball. So, when he became ten years old, he asked if he could join the Panthers' team.

146

Some of the boys on the Panthers told him he could practice with them to see whether he would be good enough to play. But they said they thought he was too little and too skinny. "You are not big enough yet," one boy said. "Maybe you can make the team next year when you are bigger."

Jimmy tried and tried to get on the team. But when the team practiced on the field every day, Jimmy did not get many chances to learn how to play. Nearly all of the time was taken for practice by boys who were bigger and better players.

One of the things Jimmy wanted most of all was a baseball suit. The team had nice suits. They were gray with black stripes, and the caps were black. On the front of each cap there was a large P. On each shirt was the word PANTHERS.

"How can I get on the team?" Jimmy would say to himself. "I want to play with the team and wear one of their nice uniforms."

Day after day Jimmy went to practice. He played as hard as he could when he got into a practice game, but he was not selected for one of the positions. Some of the other boys told him again that he was just too little and too skinny. "Wait until next year," they said. "Maybe you will be bigger and stronger. Then you may get on the team."

Jimmy felt very sad. He wanted very much to be on the team. He wanted to wear a uniform, and sit on the bench with the other boys, and go with them when they played at Brady. How could he do it?

One day he had an idea. He went to see the manager of the team and said to him, "Mr. Brown, the team needs a bat boy and someone to keep the water bucket filled. May I have that job?"

Jimmy got the job. Now he could wear a baseball uniform, sit with the team, and go with it to Brady.

When he got home that evening he told his father how he had failed to make the team and that now he was the bat boy.

His father said, "Being a bat boy is an important job. You are in charge of many things. You see that the players have fresh water to drink, you see that each player has the bat he wants, and you take care of the bats, balls, and gloves."

"But I want to be a player," said Jimmy. "I want to play first base and hit home runs."

"Well, then," said his father, "you must practice and learn how to play well. By the way, do you know that Mr. Davis, who lives next door to us, was a great ballplayer when he was a young man? He played with some of the best teams in the country. Why don't you ask him to help you?"

"I will go to see him right now," said Jimmy, and off he went.

Mr. Davis Teaches Jimmy

When Jimmy got to the house next door, he found Mr. Davis sitting on his porch. Jimmy told him how much he wanted to be a good baseball player and be on the Panther team. "Will you help me?" he said.

"Of course, I will help you," Mr. Davis said. "You and I will practice in the big field behind our house. I can show you many things a good player needs to know. Let's practice every evening. It will help me too. I need the exercise."

"When do we start?" asked Jimmy.

"Right now," said Mr. Davis.

Mr. Davis went up to the attic and got some balls, gloves, and bats that he had used when he played ball. Then he and Jimmy went off to practice.

Jimmy wanted to be a first baseman; so for several evenings they worked just on that job. Mr. Davis taught Jimmy how to hold one foot on the base when the ball was thrown to him.

Then Jimmy learned how to catch balls that were hit on the ground to him. Mr. Davis showed him how to hold his head. "You must not turn your head away," he said. "You have to look right at the ball all the time."

Mr. Davis also taught Jimmy how to move forward and backward when a grounder came toward him, so he could catch the ball when it took a big bounce.

Jimmy learned how to bat, too. He found out where he should put his feet and how to hold the bat. He learned to hold the bat up off his shoulders so it would be ready for the swing.

Mr. Davis taught Jimmy when to swing at the ball, and how to follow the ball with his eyes. He showed him where the ball has to cross home plate to be called a strike.

"One thing you must learn," Mr. Davis said, "is not to swing at bad pitches. You must wait for a pitch that will be called a strike. That kind is easier to hit."

Jimmy worked hard. He spent a lot of time with Mr. Davis, and he became a better and better player.

One day, Mr. Davis said to him, "Now, Jimmy, you should be a good enough player to get on the Panthers' team. You are hitting the ball much harder and catching grounders easily."

The Big Game

A few days later the Panthers were playing the last game of the year with the Brady Tigers. It was a big game. The two teams had played four games that year, and each team had won two of them. This game would decide the winner for the year.

On the day of the game, many people came to the field. All of the seats on both sides were filled. About two hundred people were standing or sitting on the ground.

It was an exciting day for the two teams. Both the Panthers and the Tigers wanted very much to be the champions for the year.

When the game started, Jimmy was not one of the players. Tommy Wilkins was playing first base. Tommy was older and bigger, and he had played first base in all of the games against the Tigers.

When Jimmy was not carrying water or taking care of the bats, he sat on the bench and watched the game.

It was a close game. In the third inning the Panthers made one run. But in the sixth inning the Tigers scored two runs. Then the Tigers got another run in the seventh inning. That is the way the game stood when the last inning began: Tigers–3, Panthers–1.

The Panthers went to the field for the last inning and the Tigers were at bat. The first Tiger batter did not get on base. He hit a fly that was caught by the left fielder. That made one out.

The next Tiger batter hit a hard grounder to first base. The first baseman, Tommy Wilkins, turned quickly to catch it. But, in turning so fast, he fell to the ground with a sprained ankle. Tommy could not play any more. His teammates helped him to walk to the bench, and he sat down.

Jimmy Gets a Chance

"Now, what will we do?" said the manager. "We have no other first baseman. We don't even have any more players, because all of them have been used as pinch hitters."

"What about me?" said Jimmy. "I am a first baseman."

"That's right, you are!" said the manager. "Take your glove and go in for Tommy."

What a thrill it was for Jimmy to walk out on the field! The Panthers had a new loudspeaker and a young man announced over it—"Your attention, please! Your attention, please! Number 38, Jimmy Osgood, now playing first base!"

Jimmy played his position well. He took a long throw from the shortstop for the second out, and he caught a hard grounder to make the third out.

But this was the last inning and the Tigers were still ahead, 3 to 1. The Panthers were now coming to bat for the last time.

Jimmy looked at the score card. He would be the fourth batter unless all three boys

ahead of him made outs. Then the game
would be over, and he would not get to bat
at all.

The first batter hit a fly ball to the third
baseman and made an out. But the second
batter made a two-base hit. The third batter hit a grounder that went between the
first baseman's legs. He was safe on first
base and the other boy was safe on third.

Now it was Jimmy's turn to bat. He
walked up to home plate and stood there,
just as Mr. Davis had taught him to stand.
His heart was beating fast, but he was not
afraid. "I will hit that ball," he said to
himself, "if I get a good pitch."

The pitcher looked at Jimmy and Jimmy looked at him. Then the ball came zooming in. It came so fast that Jimmy almost didn't see it.

"Strike one!" called the umpire.

Many people in the stands were now screaming at Jimmy. "Hit the ball, Jimmy!" they said. "You can do it, Jimmy!"

But Jimmy didn't hear them. He was too busy watching for the next pitch.

The pitcher threw the ball again. It was another fast one, but it was not over the plate.

"Ball one," called the umpire.

The pitcher threw another strike that
Jimmy did not swing at. Then he threw two
more balls. Now the count was three balls
and two strikes on Jimmy.

As the pitcher got ready to throw the
last pitch, the people in the stands yelled
louder than ever. "Hit it, Jimmy! Hit the
ball! You can save the game!"

Slide, Jimmy, Slide!

But Jimmy did not hear them. He just looked at the pitcher and waited. At last the pitcher let the ball go. It came in so fast it looked like a bullet. But Jimmy was ready. It was the kind of pitch he liked; so he swung his bat just as Mr. Davis had taught him to.

Smash! went the bat against the ball, and away went the ball, far into the outfield.

The boy on third came in to score, and so did the boy on first base. And Jimmy kept on running. As he passed third the coach called to him, "Run fast, Jimmy, and slide into home plate!"

Jimmy raced toward home. As he saw the ball coming in, he slid with all his might. The catcher caught the ball and tagged Jimmy with it. But he was too late!

"Safe!" yelled the umpire.

This made it four runs for Jimmy's team. The Panthers won the game—4 to 3.

At last, Jimmy had made the team. One of the first persons to come up to him was Mr. Davis. He said, "Fine hitting, Jimmy, and good sliding. Now you are a real baseball player!"

Jimmy smiled to himself as he shook the dust from his uniform.

Johnny Blair's Long Night

Johnny Blair was nine years old. At least, he had been thinking of himself as nine years old for quite a while because his mother told her friends that Johnny was "in his ninth year."

Johnny's father, on the other hand, would say that Johnny was "going on nine." And so Johnny got in the habit of thinking of himself as nine, even though he knew that his birthday was not coming for more than a month.

Johnny was going to be nine in April— to be exact, on April 16. 'Way back in March, when it was still chilly and wet, and patches of snow remained where there had been piles in the middle of the winter, Johnny began to think about his coming birthday and what he would ask for. This was a real problem, because Johnny was a very serious boy who gave such matters a good deal of careful study.

He had another problem, too. Johnny
lived in a suburb of a big city in the East.
His house was on a pleasant street lined
with trees. There was a playground a block
away, and there were many children about
his age living on his street. Johnny used
to get up early in the morning, usually
about seven o'clock, even though he did not
have to be at school until nine. He often
stood at the front window and looked into
the street, where he could see the fathers
of his friends coming out of their houses to
go off to work.

Billy Jones's father, who lived two doors
up, came out a few minutes after seven,
dressed in overalls, and drove off in his car.

He was a carpenter. Sally Martin's father, who lived across the street, came out at half-past seven, always in a hurry, and ran down the street to catch the bus at the corner. He was dressed in a business suit. He worked in an insurance office in the city.

Dicky Lewis's father, who lived four doors down the street, came out just after eight. He too was dressed in a business suit, and he drove to his work in no hurry. He worked in a big hardware store, and he did not have to get there until about nine o'clock.

Johnny's Father's Job

But Johnny Blair's father didn't go to work in the morning. He came home from work at eight o'clock!

So while Johnny was at the front window watching the fathers of his friends go off to work, fresh and clean in the early morning, his own father—well, he was sitting in the kitchen drinking coffee. He was tired, too, and his white uniform was soiled.

Mr. Blair was a milkman.

He went to work in the evening, long
after Johnny was safe asleep in his bed. He
drove a milk truck on a delivery route
through a nearby town. Starting a little
after midnight, he delivered milk until early
morning. Then he came home, had a cup
of coffee in the kitchen, and went to bed.

He slept until the middle of the afternoon
and got up about the same time that
Johnny got back from school. So he was
home to play with Johnny, and this was
very pleasant for the boy. But Johnny
didn't always have time to play with his
father. There were all those nice children

in the block, and after school was the time when they played games together.

This morning Johnny said, "Daddy, I will not be able to play with you this afternoon, because I am going over to play with Billy Jones."

"Why, that's all right, Son," said his father. "There is no reason why you should worry about not playing with me this afternoon."

Mr. Blair looked at Johnny closely. "Is something worrying you, Son?" he asked.

Johnny didn't say anything for a while. Then he said, "Well, I have been thinking about you, out in the dark all night at your job. I have been thinking that it must be a pretty lonesome job."

Mr. Blair laughed and put his hand on Johnny's shoulder. "Son, that is very kind of you, but you don't have to worry about me. I am not lonesome at all."

Johnny still looked very doubtful. "I don't see how you can help being lonesome, all alone all night, in the dark."

"Well," said Mr. Blair, "I don't know just how to explain it to you. But there is more happening on my job than you might think. I wish I could show you—."

Now this was just what Johnny had been waiting for. "You could show me, you know, if you'd take me along with you some night."

170

When Johnny Was Nine

"Oh, no!" exclaimed Johnny's mother, who had been listening. "A little boy only eight years old couldn't stay out all night!"

"Eight!" said Johnny, in a fussy tone of voice. "Eight! When you want me to run an errand, I'm a big boy almost nine. When I'm supposed to take my own bath and polish my shoes, I'm almost nine. But when I want to go out with Daddy, I'm still only eight."

Johnny's father was laughing. "The boy has a point there," he said. "We do keep on reminding him that he is almost nine."

"Still," said Mrs. Blair, "eight is very young."

Now Johnny took the next step. "For my birthday next month, I'd like to go out with Daddy on his milk route. All night. For my ninth birthday present. All night."

"Oh, dear!" said his mother.

"On Friday night," said his father, "and if he takes a nap in the afternoon, it won't hurt him a bit." Johnny's father liked to recite poetry. Now he said,

"Every child should have the
    memory
Of at least one long-after
    bedtime walk.

"That's part of a poem written by a man named Robert Frost. See what I mean, Mother?"

"Yay! Hurray, yi, yi, yi!"—And Johnny did a dance of joy about the living room.

On a warm Friday afternoon just after his birthday—it was on April 18—Johnny ran home from school and went to his room

From "The Fear" from COMPLETE POEMS OF ROBERT FROST. Copyright 1930, 1939 by Holt, Rinehart and Winston, Inc. Reprinted by permission of Holt, Rinehart and Winston, Inc., and Laurence Pollinger Ltd., Agent for Jonathan Cape Ltd.

for a nap. But he couldn't sleep. He just lay there thinking about the night ahead until someone was shaking his arm.

"Wake up, Johnny," said his father. "It's time for dinner. You have had a long nap."

As they sat down to dinner, Mr. Blair said—

"Listen, my children, and you
   shall hear
Of the midnight ride of Paul
   Revere,
On the eighteenth of April
   in Seventy-five;
Hardly a man is now alive
Who remembers that famous day
   and year.

173

"A poet by the name of Longfellow said that in a very famous poem, written a long time ago. So, Paul Revere, it's April 18. Get ready for your midnight ride."

Visiting the Dairy

So after dinner, father and son got into the family car and drove off to the big dairy. They went early to see the "plant," as Mr. Blair called it. They saw many big tins of milk that had been shipped in from the country. Also, drawn up to the loading platform, there was a big tank truck full of milk. Johnny had thought that tank trucks were only for oil or gasoline, but here was one full of milk.

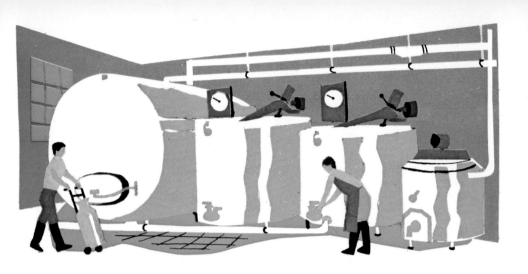

"That tank," said his father, "is lined with glass. Every day it is scoured out with strong soap and boiling water. Then it is sealed tight as the driver goes back to the country to have it refilled with milk at the country dairy."

"Then there are no cows here?" asked Johnny.

"No cows at all. Now let's go to look at the pasteurization room."

"The what room?" asked Johnny.

"I said pasteurization room. The word comes from the name of a great French scientist, Louis Pasteur. See—here it is." His father opened the door into a big room lined with gleaming, covered tanks.

"The milk is put into those tanks and heated just below the boiling point. It is kept just that hot for some time, and then there are no germs in it."

"Why don't they boil the milk?" asked Johnny.

"Because it spoils milk to boil it. Boiling makes a skin on it. You wouldn't want milk that was all full of bits of mixed-up leathery skin, would you?

"But now let's go on into the bottling room." In the bottling room they watched

big machines putting milk into bottles and capping them. Then Mr. Blair said, "Come, my truck will be all loaded and ready to go."

Outside the building there was a long row of milk trucks and men in white hurrying to them. Mr. Blair had to stop every two steps to speak to somebody. The men were all friendly and smiling. Johnny thought that they did not look very lonesome!

Delivering Milk

They drove several miles to where Mr. Blair's route began, and then he began to stop and take the milk into the backs of the dark, silent houses. After the fourth delivery, Mr. Blair came running back. "This is Mrs. Smith's, and she has left a note for two pounds of butter."

"Do you have butter?" asked Johnny.

"Indeed I do, and cream, and eggs, and several kinds of milk. I have whole milk, skimmed milk, homogenized milk—."

"Wait a minute," said Johnny. "There is another one of those long words!"

"Homogenized milk is treated so that the cream does not come to the top. Many people like it best."

Two more stops and they came to a house that was brightly lighted. Every window was shining with lights, and the sound of voices came out to Johnny and his father in the street.

"Well," said Mr. Blair, "this is a party!"

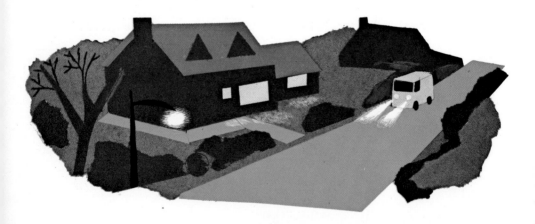

Johnny watched his father go to the back
of the house. When he leaned over to put
the milk in the box on the back porch, he
was suddenly covered with bright light. The
back door had opened, and someone was
standing in it talking to his father. Then
Mr. Blair disappeared for a moment. When
he came back to the truck he handed
Johnny a ham sandwich.

"Well, what friendly people! They wanted
me to come in for something to eat, but I
told them you were out here waiting. So
they insisted that I take two ham sand-
wiches with me." Mr. Blair drove slowly
through the warm spring night, eating his
sandwich.

They drove down a long, dark, quiet street until Mr. Blair stopped the truck again. Johnny watched him disappear into the dark beside the house. His flashlight shone brightly for a moment, and then he came running back to the truck.

"Ssh! Come with me quickly," he whispered. Johnny stepped out of the truck and followed his father to the back of the dark house.

Suddenly he turned on his flashlight, and there staring at them was a little animal with a pointed nose and what looked like a robber's mask on his face. He stared at them without moving at all.

"Ssh, he's surprised by the light. Don't move. Have you ever seen a raccoon before?"

Johnny had not seen a raccoon, and he did not know that such wild animals lived right in the city.

"He has come in to rob the garbage can," said Mr. Blair. "You'd be surprised how often I see raccoons. And I have seen a skunk, too, as well as smelled him."

Johnny learned that there are many wild animals living right in the cities. They come out at night to see whether someone has forgotten to put the lid on his garbage can. Sometimes a raccoon can pull the lid off with his strong little paws, even if it is on tight.

They went on from house to house. Once they saw a doctor with his bag hurrying into a lighted house. At another they saw a night worker in overalls going home. Then on a dark street, while Mr. Blair was at the back of a house, Johnny was suddenly blinded by a very strong light shining straight through the open window of the truck. It was pointed straight into his eyes.

The next thing he knew, a policeman was standing right by him.

"What are you doing here, young fellow?"

"Please, Sir," Johnny gulped, "I'm with my father."

Just then Mr. Blair came back to the truck. "Hello, officer, anything the matter?"

"No, Sir, I guess this young one here must be your boy."

"He certainly is," said Mr. Blair.

"Learning to be a milkman?"

"Well, no. He's just keeping me company to celebrate his ninth birthday—and to make sure that I am not lonesome."

The officer laughed. "That's a fine thing for a boy to do with his father on a warm spring night. Good day to you, Sir."

And a good day it was. The first red fingers of the sun were stealing over the housetops. A few more deliveries and Johnny and his father were finished.

As they drove home from the plant, Johnny said, "Well, Daddy, I see that you have many things and people to keep you company during the night."

"But no company as good as yours," replied his father.

Evan Kirk

Evan Kirk
Is looking for work.
Work? What can he do?
He could milk a cow
If he just knew how.
He can almost buckle a shoe.

He can count to ten
Again and again
With hardly a real mistake.
He could drive a bus
If one of us
Would handle the wheel and the brake.

He can climb a chair
When no one's there
And reach where the cookies are.
He can catch you frogs
And pollywogs
At eleven cents a jar.

For a nickel a day
He will hammer away
At woodwork, walls, and doors.
Or for nothing at all
He will paint the hall
And nail down all your floors.

The little dear
Has been working here
A year—well, almost two.
And you couldn't foresee
How glad we'd be
To send him to work on you.

—*John Ciardi*

When Snow Melts

When snow
Melts,
Twigs wear
Pearls of rain.
When one drop
Spills,
Another
Comes again.

—Adele H. Seronde

PART 5

Famous American
Women

Betsy Ross and the Flag

Young America

Two new states have been added to the United States recently, and everybody knows that our flag now has fifty stars. Alaska and Hawaii were the forty-ninth and fiftieth states.

How has the flag grown? How many stars did it have when it was first made? Who made it?

These questions take us back to the very beginning of our country's story. They take us back to the man who made the United States a free, independent country. And they take us back to the life of Betsy Ross.

But there was a lot to the story before Betsy Ross was born!

Until it was discovered by Columbus in 1492, America was a wilderness of forest, desert, and mountains. The only people were the Indians. If you could have flown over the country in an airplane, you would hardly have seen a single sign to show that people lived in North America at all.

A thin column of smoke from an Indian's fire perhaps, and not much else. Out near the deserts in Arizona and New Mexico the Indians had made large buildings, but they were exactly the same color as the earth there.

For a hundred years after Columbus there were still only Indians in North America, except for the Spanish people who came to the Southwest from Mexico. They came to the same desert lands where the states of Arizona and New Mexico now are. They built the town of Santa Fe, to which Kit Carson traveled in his first trip across the

Great Plains. They also made settlements in California.

For the next two hundred years the eastern part of North America was settled very slowly by people who came here mostly from England and Scotland. So the eastern part of the country was really owned by England. It was a colony of England. That means that the people here were not independent but were ruled by the same king that ruled England.

And it was not just one colony. Actually it was thirteen different colonies. Each one had the name that it still has today, as a state; but then it was like a separate little country. In the earliest days the people of the different colonies were not always friendly, and it was not always safe to travel from one colony to another.

But as time passed, the people of the thirteen colonies became more and more friendly. They all spoke the same English language; most of them came from England.

And they were all working to conquer the wilderness and make it safe for their children.

And they became more friendly for another reason. They did not like being ruled from England by a king who lived so far away across the ocean. The colonies all got together and declared their independence of England.

The English king sent soldiers to America to punish the colonists, and the colonists got together and made an army and fought against the soldiers from England.

They won the War for Independence. They were led by George Washington, who has been called the Father of his Country. It was a long, slow war that lasted eight years. But even before this war was over—in fact, very soon after it started—the colonies knew that they were going to unite into one country, and they needed a flag.

Planning the Flag

On June 14, 1777, the leaders of the new country, meeting in Philadelphia, passed a law. It was that the United States should have a flag with "thirteen stripes, alternate white and red, and that the Union be thirteen white stars on a blue field."

The Union is the corner of the flag where the fifty stars are now. It is sometimes used separately as a flag for boats. It is called the Union Jack now, and you will see it on a flagstaff at the front end of a boat. It is used as a signal.

After the law was passed telling what the flag should be, a committee was chosen to see about having the first flag made. General George Washington, who was to become the first President of the United States, led the committee.

Betsy Ross

Betsy Ross was named Betsy Griscom until she was married. She was one of a very large family—sixteen children! Betsy was the eighth child. When she grew up, she married John Ross and moved into a little house with him on Arch Street in Philadelphia. He ran an upholstery shop right in their house. An upholsterer repaired chairs, made pillows, covered chairs with new cloth, and even made curtains.

Betsy knew how to sew very well. In those days every girl had to learn to sew, because most people could not afford to buy their clothes. They even wove their own cloth on a loom, or they bought the cloth and sewed their own clothes. Betsy helped her husband in the shop.

George Washington and his committee came to the Rosses' shop. They all sat in front of the big fireplace in the corner of the living room and talked about the new flag for their country. The law said that it should have thirteen stripes of red and white.

Betsy began at the top with a white stripe and sewed a red one to it. Then she added a second white stripe, another red one, and so on until there were thirteen. But this made a white stripe come at the top and at the bottom, and George Washington said,

"That looks very pretty in here, but I'm afraid that the white edge will get dirty. And wouldn't it be easier to see the flag if there were a red stripe at the top and the bottom?"

One of the other men said it would be a pity to make Betsy start all over again.

"Oh, I don't have to start all over," said Betsy. "I'll just add a red stripe to the top of the flag and take the white one off the bottom." It took her only a few minutes to do this. When she had finished there were seven red stripes and six white ones. They stood for the thirteen states.

Next they talked about the stars. George Washington thought they should have six-pointed stars, but Betsy said, "A five-pointed star is prettier, and let me show you how to cut one."

She folded up a bit of white cloth and with one snip of her scissors made a perfect five-pointed star. Everybody liked the five-pointed star and agreed that it was what they would have on the flag. So Betsy cut out thirteen stars while the committee sat before the fire and talked. That didn't take her more than a few minutes, either.

Next they discussed the blue field up in the corner. They decided that it should be as wide as the top seven stripes, and that is

the way Betsy cut it. After she had sewed the blue field over the stripes in the corner, to show how it would look in place, she cut out the space for it.

After several trials, they agreed to put the stars in a circle, and that was the way the first flag was made.

With this start, Betsy got more orders for flags. The Government gave her an order to make all of its flags. She made hundreds of flags during the next fifty years, right up until she was 75 years old.

The Flag Is Changed

After the War for Independence, a problem came up. New states wanted to join the United States. The first two to join the thirteen states were Vermont and Kentucky. That made fifteen states in the United States. But the law said that there should be a stripe on the flag for each state.

So Betsy began making flags with fifteen stripes. Each stripe had to be a little narrower, if they were all to go into the same space. Betsy wondered what the flag would look like if it had a great many narrow stripes instead of the thirteen wide ones.

The Government began to think about the same problem, too, and when five more states asked to join the Union, it decided that thirteen stripes were enough. So it passed a new law that the thirteen stripes should stand for the first thirteen states, which have always been called the Thirteen Original States.

Some years later, when there were more states, there was not room in the circle for all the stars. So the last change was made. The stars were put in lines—and that is the way the flag still is, with a star added to one of the lines every time a new state is added to the United States.

"The Star-Spangled Banner"

Our flag is called "The Star-Spangled Banner." That means a flag decorated with stars. Spangles are shining decorations, and sometimes it seems as if the stars on the flag shine.

A man named Francis Scott Key first called the flag that when he watched it flying all night over a fort that was being shot at by English warships. He was held prisoner in an English warship.

As he watched the battle, he could see the flag by the light of the "bombs bursting in air" and by the light of "the rockets' red glare." He put these words into the song that you sing so many times and hear so many times more.

People liked the song so much when they first heard it that it was soon made the country's special or "official" song. That is why we call it the National Anthem. Anthem is another word for song. It means a very serious song.

Louisa May Alcott

Little Women

One of the most famous and delightful stories ever written is *Little Women*. It has been read with laughter, and with tears, by thousands upon thousands of young men and young girls. Most of all by girls, who laugh and cry over it when they are ten or twelve or even fourteen years old.

Grown-ups read it, too, with the same pleasure. It is the story of a family of four sisters—Jo, Amy, Beth, and Meg March—their adventures, their work, their hopes and fears, and the wonderful time they had living together in a tiny town in Massachusetts.

Louisa May Alcott wrote this book about herself and her family. She later told people who asked that she put herself in the story as Jo March. Her sisters are the other three March girls in the story. But she did not write it until long after she was a young girl. She did not have an easy life, and she had to go through many hardships before she became a famous writer and earned a great deal of money from the sale of her books.

How Louisa Grew Up

Louisa's father was Bronson Alcott. He was a famous teacher who wanted to make school a happy place, back in the days when school was usually nothing but hard work—and punishment if the lessons were not properly learned. Nearly all schools were private in those days. Some were run by churches. Others were run by teachers, who made very little money from them.

There were no large public schools, such as we have today, and not very many small ones. Girls did not generally go to school. They learned to read at home. If the parents had enough money, boys were sent to private teachers or private schools. Sometimes a teacher would go from home to home, teaching the children in each home for just the food and bed that the family could give him.

Yet almost everybody learned to read, and the people of those times read a great deal. Bronson Alcott had his special ideas about making school friendly and happy, but many people thought that school should be strict and hard. They would not send their children to his school, so he did not get along very well.

Louisa was born in Philadelphia. When she was still a little girl, her father's school lost all its pupils, and there was no money for the family to live on. So they took the boat from Philadelphia to Boston, and there Mr. Alcott started another school.

In Boston Louisa became a tomboy. She ran in the streets and played in the big park in the center of the city. She could run as fast as any boy. Once she ran so fast and so far with her hoop that she lost her way and had to be brought home by the police. The policeman found her asleep in a doorway, with a strange dog beside her.

The dog was sleeping, too, and was keeping himself warm with his head in her lap.

Things went well for a while, but then this new school lost its pupils, and when Louisa was only seven the family moved to Concord, Massachusetts. This was a very small town just a few miles from Boston, but it was full of many famous people whom you will read about as you go through school.

Although the family had to live in a very tiny house, Louisa loved Concord because all around it were fields and woods. She could run in them and be as free as the wind. When she was only eight, Louisa wrote a poem:

To a Robin

Welcome, welcome, little stranger,
Fear no harm, and fear no danger;
We are glad to see you here,
For you sing "Sweet Spring is near."

By the time she was twelve she had written dozens of plays that she acted with her sisters. They used the barn for a theater, and they built a little stage at one end of it. Their friends loved to come in and watch the Alcott girls act the plays, which were full of excitement and adventure. They were about pirates, and robberies, and distant places that Louisa had never seen.

Even though she spent a lot of time reading and writing, Louisa was still a tomboy. Here is what she wrote about herself in *Little Women,* many years later. Her sister Amy said that it was not ladylike to whistle, and Jo (who, you will remember, was Louisa herself) replied this way. See whether you can understand this little bit from the book:

> "I hate affected, niminy-
> piminy chits! I'm not a
> young lady; and if turning
> up my hair makes me one,
> I'll wear it in two tails
> till I'm twenty. I hate
> to think I've got to grow
> up, and be *Miss* March, and
> wear long gowns, and look
> as prim as a china aster!
> It's bad enough to be a
> girl, anyway, when I like
> boys' games and work and
> manners!"

But life in Concord was very hard. The
Alcott family—now four small girls and the
two parents—had to live almost on what
grew in their own garden. They often had
nothing but bread for breakfast, and bread
and potatoes or squash for dinner. Mr. Alcott invited two friends to live with them,
when there was not enough room or food
for the family! He was a very generous
man, but he was not very careful or practical. He liked to talk, and he would sit up
talking all night with his friends. All the
children loved him very much.

Louisa worked and worked at her writing, even though she did not have a room of her own where she could write in peace and quiet. When she was sixteen, she wrote a whole book, called *Flower Fables*. It was printed, and many people liked it. The same year she went to work.

Teaching and Writing

She became a school teacher, like her father, in Boston. She took care of children. She acted as a private teacher for young girls. She did sewing at night to earn a little more money. And always in any free minute she worked at writing stories, for more than anything else in the world she wanted to be a writer.

212

When she was nineteen, one of her stories was printed in a magazine. She was paid five dollars for it. Then more stories were printed, and a book of fairy tales that she made up herself. Later, she almost had a play acted by a real company of actors. But by bad luck the manager of the actors fell and broke his leg, and he had to change his plans. So the play was never acted.

One day a great thing happened to Louisa. She had sold a second story to the magazine that had printed her first story.

Then came a taste of the fame that she hoped for. She has written about the day, which she said was one of the most exciting in her life. It was a wintry day in New England, and Louisa was trudging to her school in the pale gray light of early morning.

Suddenly her eye, as she told the story, "fell upon a large poster with these delicious words,

'Bertha, a New Tale by the Author of the *Rival Prima Donnas,* Will Appear in the *Saturday Evening Gazette.*'"

Louisa was late to school, and the day was bitter cold, but she stood there on the sidewalk, pushed and bumped by the hurrying crowd, feasting her eyes on the wonderful poster. Being very shy, she was afraid of being recognized by someone, but she could not take her eyes off the poster. She hugged herself with joy and said, "This, this is fame!"

That day in school her pupils had an easy time of it, for Louisa was lost in daydreams of fame.

"While they struggled with their pothooks," she later wrote, "I was writing immortal works."

Louisa knew a great many words, for she had been reading since she was four or five years old. By "pothooks" she meant the penmanship or handwriting of her little pupils. "Immortal" means that something will never die, and Louisa was saying that she would write books that would be read forever.

After school that day Louisa ran home and told her family about the wonderful poster, and they came back with her to look at it. Finding it torn by the wind, they boldly stole it and carried it home. It was kept as a family treasure for many years.

For ten years Louisa went on with her teaching and writing. Most of her stories were printed, and she earned some money, but she did not think that what she was writing was as good as she could do. Her family needed all the money that she could earn.

A Famous Writer

The War Between the States broke out when Louisa was about thirty years old, and like Florence Nightingale, she became a nurse. She had many adventures caring for the sick and the wounded. Later, when she was back home again, she wrote a book called *Hospital Sketches*.

Two years later, her father gathered together a number of her stories and took them to a publisher (a man who printed and sold books) to see whether he would not put them together into a book.

But the publisher suggested in return that Louisa try writing a book for girls. Louisa had already written two books, called novels, that had not been very successful, but she set about trying once more.

In two months she wrote the first part of *Little Women.* It was published in 1868. A few months later the second part was ready —and, after so many years of hard work, Louisa found herself famous.

When her second novel, *Little Men,* was ready, the public ordered fifty thousand copies of it before it was published. They wanted to be sure to have the new book by the author of *Little Women.*

After this success, Louisa wrote many more books. She was a rich and famous woman, and she is still known and loved by the thousands of girls and boys who read her books every year.

Some day you may take a trip to Concord, Massachusetts, where not only Louisa
May Alcott but also several others of the
greatest American writers lived. It is still a
tiny town, and on a quiet street you may
visit the little house where the Alcott family lived. It is now a museum, where you
may look at many things that will make
you remember the little women who lived
there more than a hundred years ago.

Marian Anderson—Lady
From Philadelphia

The sun burned down on the cobblestone streets and brick sidewalks of Philadelphia that summer day in 1919, but teen-aged Marian Anderson, waiting on the corner for

Adapted from MARIAN ANDERSON: Lady From Philadelphia, by Shirlee P. Newman. The Westminster Press. Copyright © 1966 Shirlee P. Newman. Used by permission.

a trolley, hardly felt the heat. As the big, green streetcar jolted to a stop, Marian sprang up the steps, smiled at the perspiring motorman, and dropped a coin into the fare box.

The car lurched forward, and Marian made her way past men and women crowded together on either side of the aisle, talking about the humidity, fanning themselves with straw hats or folded newspapers.

A stout woman sitting in the back moved over to make room for Marian. "My, you look cheerful for such a scorcher!" she said.

"Thank you." Marian squeezed into the empty seat and smoothed down the collar of her freshly ironed blouse. Who cared that it was hot? This was the day she had been looking forward to for most of her life—today she was going to enroll in the music school uptown! As the trolley jangled in and out of the narrow streets, she began to hum softly.

To Marian, singing was as natural as speaking. In fact, she would rather sing. She had been able to carry a tune since high

chair days, and when she was about seven she had joined the junior choir at the Union Baptist Church near her home in South Philadelphia. She and Viola Johnson, another girl in the choir, had become friends, and one Sunday they sang a duet together.

"Viola's voice sounded like skimmed milk," Marian's father, who was dead now, had told her mother. "Marian's voice was like corned beef and cabbage."

Indeed, Marian sang low notes so well that visitors from other churches took word of the "Baby Contralto" back to their own congregations, and before long, she was invited to sing in churches all over the city.

A Musical Child

She'd been a quiet child with a thin face. Now, as a teen-ager, she was tall and graceful. Her face, heart-shaped, and with suggestions of dimples in her cheeks, was framed by long hair falling to her shoulders in gentle waves. Her eyes were large, dark, luminous, and when she sang, they brightened with sparks of joy. From the beginning, music was Marian Anderson's life.

Marian's inborn love of music also showed itself in forms other than singing. Looking out of the trolley window, she noticed they were passing the pawnshop around the corner from where she used to live. She smiled, recalling how, when she was six and no taller than the hydrant in front of the shop, she'd spied a violin hanging in the cluttered window.

Just like the one the man plays in church, she'd thought. She could still remember the jingle of the bells dangling from the knob as

she pushed open the door. It was dark inside, and the jumble of merchandise was covered with soot.

"P—please, Mister," she said to the pawnbroker peering down at her through thick tortoise-rimmed spectacles, "how much would I need to buy the violin?"

"Three dollars and forty-five cents," he replied, summoning as businesslike a tone as he could, considering the size of the customer. "Do you think you can afford it?"

"No. That must be an awful lot of money." She backed out the door carefully to avoid disturbing the bells again. "But I'll try to earn it," she added.

The next day, her mother's scrub pail swinging from her arm, Marian reached up and rang a neighbor's doorbell. "I'll rub and I'll scrub, and make your steps clean," she recited, when the lady of the house appeared. And she fulfilled her promise.

On hands and knees, she scrubbed those stone steps till they shone! The delighted woman paid her a nickel and recommended her services highly. Penny by penny, nickel by nickel, months later, Marian had enough money. She went back to the pawnshop and bought the violin. A friend of the family taught her how to tune it and play a few notes, but it wasn't long before the strings snapped and the bridge cracked in two. Sitting on the streetcar, Marion remembered now how quickly her career as a violinist had ended. Later, her father bought her an old upright piano but there was not enough money to pay for piano lessons.

Singing was what Marian liked best. When she was thirteen, she was transferred from the junior to the senior choir. Now she sang

for the Y.M.C.A. and other organizations around town. Sometimes she was paid to sing, usually twenty-five or fifty cents, and once in a while, a whole dollar!

Nature had blessed Marian with a glorious voice, but to be a good singer, she needed to have voice training. The people at her church had agreed to pay for her lessons. So, Marian was now on the way to enroll in a school of music.

When she arrived at the school, she took her place in the line of girls waiting to register and when her turn came, she said to the office girl, "Good morning, I would like—"

The office girl looked past her as if she weren't there. "Would you like an application blank?" she asked the girl behind Marian. Then she called the next girl . . . and the next.

When no one else was left, Marian once again stepped to the window. "What do you want?" asked the girl behind a desk.

"I'd like an application blank, please," said Marian.

"We don't take colored." BANG . . . the window came down in Marian's face.

Knees shaking, Marian turned around and walked out.

Singing Lessons

All the way home, Marian wondered why the music school did not take colored students. At last, the motorman called her stop and she got off. She paused a minute to watch some laughing, shouting children stripped to their underwear run in and out of the fountain of water that was gushing high from an open fire hydrant.

A tiny girl about four years old stood on the sidelines. She would step forward as if to join in the fun, but then she'd stop, afraid of the crush of the older children. Suddenly a tall boy boosted her to his shoulders, and waving everyone else out of the way, pranced her into the cooling water. The girl shrieked with delight. She was Negro. The boy was white.

"Black and white children *play* together," thought Marian as she went on home. "Why can't they also study music together?"

At last something happened that made Marian think there was a chance to make singing her career. When she was a junior in high school, she met Mary Patterson, a good singer who lived nearby and who had studied uptown with a vocal teacher. Mrs. Patterson listened to Marian sing and offered to give her lessons without charge.

Singing lessons at last! Marian was thrilled. When she had studied with Mrs. Patterson for a few months, her new teacher suggested that the girl make a change.

"Marian, I've taught you all I can," she said. "Now you should be studying with someone else."

Shortly before Marian's graduation from high school, Dr. Lucy Wilson, her principal, arranged for her to meet Giuseppe Boghetti, a well-known vocal coach who had trained many famous concert singers and opera stars.

When Boghetti heard Marian sing, he was so pleased that he agreed at once to work with her.

"I will need only two years with you," he told Marian. "After that you will be able to go anywhere, sing for anybody."

Marian worked very hard at her music and soon was singing for important organizations. She began to receive fees of fifty dollars a night. By the time she was twenty, she was making enough money to buy her mother a home of her own.

At last she was invited to sing a concert at Town Hall in New York. And then she went on concert tours with Billy King, an excellent pianist, as her accompanist.

Her Fame Spreads

Marian's fame as a singer grew from year to year. She sang at Carnegie Hall, went to London and Germany to study, and then she was invited to appear in a concert tour of several European cities. On this tour she sang in Oslo, Helsinki, Copenhagen, Stockholm, and in several other great cities. The following year she sang in London, Salzburg, Geneva, Paris, and Vienna.

Soon after she came back to the United States in 1937, she was invited to sing at the White House for President and Mrs. Franklin D. Roosevelt. Mrs. Roosevelt had graciously invited Marian's mother to attend.

As they entered the music room, President

Roosevelt looked up from his big, comfortable sofa beside a roaring fire, smiled broadly, and said: "Why, hello there, Miss Anderson. You look just like your photographs, don't you?"

That was one of the few times in her career that Marian ever felt flustered. She was so tongue-tied she couldn't recite the little speech she had prepared.

But the President's friendly handshake and warm welcome made her feel completely at ease again.

When she finished singing, Mrs. Roosevelt put the crowning touch on the occasion. Taking Marian's mother by the hand, she led her across the room and introduced her to the President!

In the next several years, Marian was one of the most famous singers of the world. She sang in all kinds of places, from palaces to big, outdoor stadiums. She sang for the famous. She sang for the humble.

One of the occasions that pleased her most was when she sang on Easter Sunday 1939, at the Lincoln Memorial in Washington, D.C. Thousands of people stood in the sunshine to hear her.

When Marian, standing alone before the huge statue of Lincoln, had sung the "Ave Maria," the shouting would not die down, the audience loved her so much.

Marian never realized how well known she was throughout the world. In 1953, she went on a singing tour of South America and Japan.

"There must be an important person on board," she said to a friend when she saw the big crowd waiting for the plane at the Tokyo Airport.

There was! Marian Anderson. It never occurred to her that so many people were waiting to greet her.

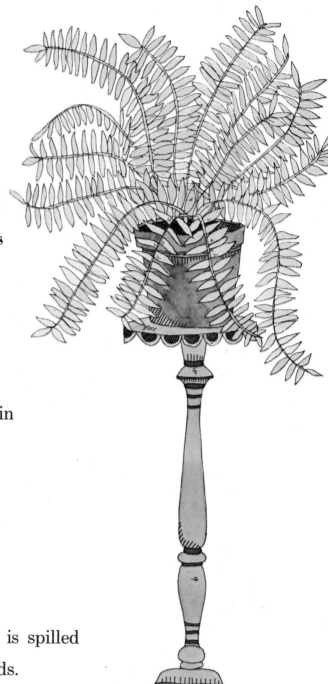

Ferns

Pale furls
Of green
Are seen
Uncurl.
Ferns will unspin
In spiral swirls.

Frail fronds
Unfold.
The cold
Responds
To sun. Winter is spilled
In swelling ponds.

—Adele H. Seronde

236

Quiver, Shiver

Quiver,
Shiver,
   aspen leaves,
Tremble,
Twitch,
   and quake;
Catch a sliver
   of the sun,
A shimmer
   of the lake!

—*Adele H. Seronde*

237

Boats Sail on the Rivers

Boats sail on the rivers,
  And ships sail on the seas;
But clouds that sail across the sky
  Are prettier far than these.
There are bridges on the rivers,
  As pretty as you please;
But the bow that bridges heaven,
  And overtops the trees,
And builds a road from earth to sky,
  Is prettier far than these.

—Christina Rossetti

PART 6

Famous
Women
of
Other
Lands

Florence Nightingale

Today boys and girls go to school to-gether, work together, and play together. They work in factories, in offices, and in stores. Girls as well as boys become writers, doctors, lawyers, and scientists. Girls fly air-planes, make daring jumps in parachutes, and even drive taxicabs.

Women vote, of course, just as men do; and they hold many important positions in our government. Women are ambassadors to foreign countries. They have been governors, senators, and members of the House of Rep-resentatives in Washington.

Women have become famous athletes. They skate, ski, and drive racing cars. Some women even go in for professional wrestling, and the rough sport of roller-derby skating.

Women today can do just about anything that they are able to do. We do not see many women driving trucks, laying bricks, or working in coal mines; but nobody says they absolutely cannot.

Not many years ago, women were generally expected to stay at home cooking, housecleaning, and caring for their children. They were expected to be polite and to be good company, but not to worry about "important" things. They were not allowed to vote. They were not urged to go to high school or college. It was not possible for them to become doctors.

The freedom that girls and women enjoy today has been won for them by the bravery and energy of great and famous women in the past.

A Young Girl

Florence Nightingale was one of the greatest of these women. She was born in 1820, in Italy. But she was not Italian. She was the daughter of two rich and important English people. Her father owned a great deal of land in England. Her mother was the daughter of a man who was both rich and famous. His name was William Smith, and he was in the English government for many years.

Her family lived, most of the time, in a great house in the middle of England. Where they lived was called an estate. There were miles and miles of their lands, all fenced off. They had dozens of servants, dozens of horses to ride, and many buildings. They even owned the houses in which the people lived who grew their food and tended their cattle. So there was really a little town on the Nightingale estate.

Florence was rich, pretty, and protected in the great family estate in Derbyshire. She was taught by her father and by private teachers, who were brought to the estate just to teach her. She traveled all over Europe when she was a young girl and learned French, German, and Italian.

Florence seemed to be raised for a life of fun and games and parties.

—But she did not like them.

She would steal off from a great family party and go to visit some sick person on the estate. Always she was more interested in helping the poor and the sick than in playing games and enjoying herself. She was more eager to pity the sick than to meet successful and famous people.

When she was still very young, she learned that a beautiful sheep dog had been injured. This fine dog belonged to a shepherd who worked for her father. The dog could understand any command and obey it. All by himself he could guide a flock of sheep down from the mountain, where they were grazing, and into their pen for the night.

Now the dog was hurt. The shepherd thought he had broken one of his legs and was sadly planning to kill him, for in those days no one knew how to take care of a broken leg on an animal. When little Florence heard about this, she went to see the injured animal. She discovered that his leg was not broken but just bruised. She cared for the dog for days, until he was completely well again and back at work herding sheep for the shepherd.

Florence Helps the Sick

When Florence's family went down to London, the great city of England, for a season of parties, dances, and music, Florence used to steal away from the fun and visit hospitals. When the family traveled abroad, Florence tried to help the poor and sick of any country they visited.

As she grew older, her interest in helping the sick increased. She studied the hospitals of France, Germany, and Italy to see how the sick were cared for in each of these lands. In Germany she met Pastor Fliedner,

who had started a great hospital there. Pastor Fliedner had spent his life helping the poor and the sick. He became so well known that many people gave him money for his work, and he was able to start this great hospital. Florence worked and studied with Pastor Fliedner. When she finished, he said that she was the best student he had ever had.

When Florence returned to England, she would not live in the comfort of Lea Hurst. (That was the name of the family estate.) There was too much to be done among the sick and the poor. She heard that a home for sick servants, in London, was about to close because it did not have enough money.

Florence left her beautiful home and went there to live and help. She helped both with her own money and with her own work.

Nursing the Soldiers

At this time England was fighting a war with Russia. It was called the Crimean War, and it took place down near the southern edge of Russia, near the Black Sea. The English soldiers were not properly clothed for the cold. They were not fed properly. And they did not have proper care from doctors and nurses.

Indeed, this was the time when there were not very many women working as nurses. The wounded English soldiers were kept in dirty hospitals, without proper care, or bandages, or food, and most of them died.

During the winter of 1854, the snow in the Crimea was three feet deep, and many soldiers froze to death in their thin tents.

Something had to be done. Florence Nightingale was well known by this time for her work with the poor and the sick. She was put in charge of a group of about 35 nurses, whom she agreed to lead on this hard and dangerous task.

When people heard that she was going, they made a heroine of her. The poor fishermen's wives in France carried the boxes and trunks of Florence and her nurses from the boat to the train that was to take them all the way across Europe to Turkey. These poor women were pleased and proud to see another woman doing work that had, until then, been done mostly by men. They were proud to see a woman taking an important place in the world of work and danger.

In the English hospital in Turkey, Florence and her nurses found hundreds and hundreds of wounded men dying of dirt, hunger, lack of care, and disease. The men had been carried in ships over the Black Sea, five days from the battle, without any medicine or care. No wonder these men were dying.

At first Florence met the problem that you have read about in the first pages of this story. The men in charge of the army hospitals did not think that women should be allowed to go into such work. They thought the women were "interfering" in men's work. But Florence was such a good manager, and so good at working with people, that she soon was put in complete charge of the wounded men. She was given the right to command just as if she were an officer.

She directed the army in setting up a
huge kitchen that could feed 800 sick men
the special meals they had to have in order
to get well. Then she started a laundry.
She saw to it that the beds were repaired,
that clean sheets were supplied, and that
books and games were there for the men
who were getting well enough to enjoy
themselves.

And she worked! It is told that she
stayed awake all night more than once, going from bed to bed, that she seemed to
know every wounded man's name, and that
she was always present when the need for
her was greatest.

In a year and a half, until the war ended, she saved the lives of more and more men. When she came, sixty of every hundred wounded men died. By the end of the year and a half, only one man in a hundred wounded was dying. Many lives were saved because of her hard work, work that all the people in England heard about.

Florence Becomes Famous

When the war came to an end, the government sent a special boat for Florence Nightingale, and the people of England prepared to give her a heroine's welcome. They planned to have a parade, with cannons firing and flags waving.

But Florence was shy about such celebrations. She took a different ship from France and went secretly to the family estate, Lea Hurst, without being seen by anyone.

But the Queen of England, Queen Victoria, rewarded Florence with a wonderful present. It was a beautiful rich enamel pin decorated with rubies and diamonds. The pin was made specially to honor this great

woman. And shortly after, the government gave a very large sum of money to build a hospital where nurses could be trained. It was named the Nightingale Training School in St. Thomas' Hospital. The hospital still stands in London.

Florence was given many other rewards and honors. She was called by the men she helped, "The Angel of the Crimea," for she seemed like an angel to the sick and wounded men so far from home. Her memory still lives in the hearts of many English men and women.

Jenny Lind

A Poor Little Girl

Jenny Lind was born in Sweden in 1820. Her family was very poor, for her father would rather drink and sing than work, and her mother made very little money teaching school. Her mother was so poor that she had to send Jenny to live in a home that was paid for by the Swedish church. This home was a few miles from Stockholm, the capital of Sweden. Later she went to the school where her mother taught.

One day when Jenny was still very young, she heard the bugles of an army band playing in the street. She went to the piano and played the tune that she had heard on the bugles. Her grandmother, who lived with them, thought it must be Jenny's older sister, Amelia, playing, for Jenny had never had any piano lessons. When her grandmother called to her, Jenny was frightened and hid behind the piano.

The grandmother thought that Jenny should have music lessons because she could hear and remember a tune so well. But the poor family did not have the money for music lessons. They did not even have enough money for food. Jenny's mother had to give up her teaching and go to work as a servant, teaching and taking care of the children of a rich family.

She took the older sister, Amelia, to live with her. Jenny's grandmother had to go into a home for old people, and she took Jenny there to live with her.

Jenny loved her grandmother, and she was too young to worry much about being poor. She had a pet cat to whom she loved to sing, and she would sit by the window in the home, joyfully singing for everyone who

passed to hear. She was heard one day by a girl who was the maid of a dancer at the Swedish Royal Opera House.

This maid told her mistress that she had never heard such beautiful singing, and the dancer herself walked by the home to hear Jenny sing. She was just as excited as her maid had been. She went to Jenny's mother and told her that Jenny must be trained and educated to become an actress.

But these were the times when women did not have the freedom they have today. Acting was not thought proper for a lady. Jenny's mother firmly refused to let the child be educated for the stage. "But at least," insisted Miss Lundberg, the dancer, "you must have her trained in singing."

Jenny Learns to Sing

She insisted so strongly that at last Mrs. Lind let her take Jenny to sing for the singing master of the Royal Theater in Stockholm. He was so delighted with her singing that he started to teach her right away. She was taken into the Royal Theater, and from then on she was supported by the Swedish government.

For the next ten years, Jenny studied at the Royal Theater. Since her food, clothes, and room were paid for by the government, Jenny's mother insisted that she come back home to live—and pay for it. Her mother was so harsh and severe that Jenny ran away from home, but she had to go back.

Finally, when she was eighteen, Jenny was ready to sing before a real audience. Her first songs had the audience shouting, crying, and clapping. Never had they heard such beautiful singing. Jenny was famous overnight. She sang in operas (they are plays in which all the parts are sung rather than spoken), and she was seen by the King of Sweden himself.

When she was twenty, Jenny decided to go to Paris so that she could study under the greatest singing teacher in the world, Manuel Garcia.

The life of a singer is not easy. Jenny had been working so hard, singing night after night, that her voice was tired and not pretty. When she sang for Manuel Garcia, he said that "It would be useless to teach you, Miss. You have no voice left."

Jenny later said that this was the most unhappy moment of her life. But she asked Garcia what to do, and he told her to give her voice a rest for six weeks—not singing at all, and hardly talking.

After her rest, Garcia listened to her sing again and agreed to teach her. Jenny studied with him for almost a year. From that time on, Jenny sang to one delighted audience after another in all the great cities of Europe. When a concert by her was advertised, the demand for tickets was likely to be four times as large as the number of seats in the theater. The Queen of England threw a wreath of flowers at her feet when she sang in London. Kings and princes praised her.

But Jenny was always kind and tender. Once she met a very old woman who was walking up and down in front of the poor-house where she lived. "What do you need most?" Jenny asked her.

"I have lived a long, long time," said the woman, "and desire nothing more before I die but to hear Jenny Lind."

"And would it make you happy?" asked Jenny.

"Ay, that it would; but such folks as I can't go to the playhouse; so I will never hear her."

"Don't be so sure of that," said the other, leading her into the house. "Sit down and listen."

When she had finished her song, Jenny said, "Now you have heard Jenny Lind," and she hurried away without letting the old woman thank her.

Jenny made a great deal of money from her concerts, but she gave most of it to poor people.

Jenny Goes to America

So great was her fame in Europe that P.T. Barnum was determined to bring her to the United States. Barnum was the man who started the traveling circus in America. He was also famous for the many stunts and tricks he worked up to entertain people. He made a great fortune getting people to spend their money coming to his shows.

Now he offered Jenny Lind the most money she had ever been paid. He offered her one thousand dollars a night to sing at one hundred fifty concerts all over the United States.

Barnum had a great deal of trouble raising the money to bring Jenny here, for he had to have all the money in the bank before Jenny would come across the ocean. He finally borrowed the money, although people said that he would lose it all.

The Swedish Nightingale

But they were mistaken, for Jenny was even more popular in America than she had been in Europe. The people of the United States loved her. Both she and Barnum made hundreds of thousands of dollars. For her first concert, in New York, the tickets were sold at auction, and the bidding went up to $650 for a single ticket. Jenny made nearly ten thousand dollars from this concert. She gave most of it to the mayor of New York, to be given by him to poor people. Everybody was talking about Jenny Lind, and huge crowds gathered to look at her whenever it was known that she would pass a certain spot.

Jenny married the man who took charge of her concerts. She raised a family and lived to see her grandchildren.

Jenny Lind, who was born in the same year as Florence Nightingale, 1820, was called "the Swedish Nightingale." But this does not mean that she was named after Florence Nightingale. The nightingale is a songbird. It is the European cousin of the American mockingbird, and it has the most beautiful song of any bird in Europe. That is why Jenny Lind was called the Swedish Nightingale.

Get Up or You'll be Late for School, Silly!

Someone I know—and he's very near—
Someone I know who lives right here,
Someone I know with a pumpkin head,
Someone right here in this bed,

Would like me to think he is sound asleep.
Would like me to think he is far and deep
With his nose in the pillow. Would like me
  to think
I didn't see him—quick as a wink—

Duck back into bed as I came in.
I saw him all right. I saw him grin.
He is grinning right now. And how do I know?
Maybe a grin-bird told me so.

Or it just may be that his grin has spread
Around his face to the back of his head.
Why, so it has! Oh dear! Oh dear!
I've heard of grinning from ear to ear,

But never before have I ever found
A grin that goes the whole way round
The back of the neck. If he grins any more,
His head will fall off and roll on the floor.

Well, if anyone is there in that bed,
If anyone's home in that pumpkin head,
And if whoever it is, is you—
You had better get up!

              —Well! How do you do?

                    —John Ciardi

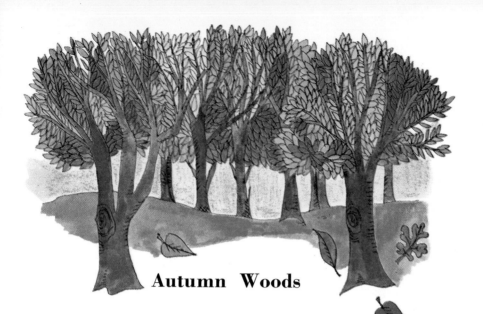

Autumn Woods

I like the woods
   In autumn
When dry leaves hide the ground,
When the trees are bare
And the wind sweeps by
With a lonesome rushing sound.

I can rustle the leaves
   In autumn
And I can make a bed
In the thick dry leaves
That have fallen
From the bare trees
Overhead.

—James S. Tippett

Glossary

absolutely

ab so lute ly (ab′sə lut′lē), positively. *adv.*

ac ci dent (ak′sə dənt), an event not wanted, intended, or planned to happen. *n.*

ac com pa nist (ə kum′pə-nist), person who plays a musical part added to help or enrich the main part. *n.*

ac tress (ak′tris), a woman who acts on the stage, in motion pictures, television, etc. *n.*

a dult (ə dult′ or ad′ult), grown-up. *adj.*

ad ven ture (ad ven′chər), 1. a bold and difficult under-taking, usually exciting and somewhat dangerous. 2. an unusual experience. *n.*

ad ver tise (ad′vər tīz), an-nounce to the public. *v.*

af fect ed (ə fek′tid), not nat-ural; artificial. *adj.*

a gree ment (ə grē′ment), an agreeing; an understanding reached by two or more per-sons or groups. *n.*

arrest

air mail (ār′ māl), the system of sending mail by aircraft. *adj.*

al ter nate (ôl′tər nit), first one and then the other by turns: *The row has alter-nate squares and circles. adj.*

a maze ment (ə māz′mənt), great surprise; sudden won-der. *n.*

am bas sa dor (am bas′ə dər), a representative of highest rank sent by one govern-ment or ruler to another. *n.*

an gri ly (ang′grə lē), in an angry manner. *adv.*

an oth er (ə nuℊ′ər), one more. *adj.*

an swer (an′sər), speak or write words in return to a question. *v.*

an them (an′thəm), song of praise, devotion, or patriot-ism. *n.*

ant ler (ant′lər), 1. horn of a deer. 2. branch of a deer's horn. *n.*

a part ment (ə pärt′mənt), room or group of rooms to live in. *n.*

ap pli ca tion (ap′lə kā′shən), a request. *n.*

ar rest (ə rest′), take to jail or court. *v.*

hat, āge, cãre, fär; let, ēqual, tėrm; it, īce; hot, ōpen, ôrder; oil, out; cup, pùt, rüle, ūse; ch, child; ng, long; th, thin; ℊ, then; zh, measure; ə represents *a* in about, *e* in taken, *i* in pencil, *o* in lemon, *u* in circus.

a round (ə round'), in a circle
about. *adv.*

as pen (as'pən), a kind of pop-
lar tree whose leaves tremble and rustle in the slight-
est breeze. *n.*

as ter (as'tər), a common
flower with white, pink, or
purple petals around a yellow center. *n.*

ath lete (ath'lēt), person
trained in exercises of
strength, speed, and skill.
Baseball players and boxers
are athletes. *n.*

auc tion (ôk'shən), public sale
in which each thing is sold
to the person who offers the
most money for it. *n.*

au di ence (ô'dē əns), people
gathered in a place or building to hear or see. *n.*

a wak en (ə wāk'ən), wake
up, rouse from sleep. *v.*

boost (büst), to lift or push
from below or behind. *v.*

brace (brās), give firmness to;
support. *v.*

branch (branch), part of a
tree that grows out from
the trunk. *n.*

brand (brand), 1. mark made
by burning the skin with a
hot iron. 2. to mark by
burning the skin with a hot
iron. *n. v.*

brave (brāv), a North American Indian warrior. *n.*

break fast (brek'fəst), the
first meal of the day. *n.*

breed (brēd), race; stock. *n.*

buck (buk), male deer. *n.*

bud (bud), 1. the small beginning of a flower, leaf, or
branch. 2. a flower partly
opened. *n.*

bugle (bū'gəl), a musical in-
strument like a small trum-
pet. *n.*

band age (ban'dij), a strip of
cloth or other material used
in dressing and binding up a
wound, injured leg or arm,
etc. *n.*

beau ti ful (bū'tə fəl), very
pleasing to see or hear. *adj.*

blare (blār), make a loud,
harsh sound. *v.*

bleat (blēt), a cry made by a
sheep, goat, or calf, or a
sound like it. *n.*

bold (bōld), without fear. *adj.*

can cel (kan'səl), mark so
that it cannot be used
again. *v.*

cap i tal (kap'ə təl), the city
where the government of a
country or state is located.
n.

card board (kärd' bôrd'), a
stiff material made of paper
and used for making boxes,
etc. *n.*

care ful ly (kãr'fəl ē), in a
thorough manner. *adv.*

272

cat a logue (kat′ə lôg), a list. *n.*

cham pi on (cham′pē ən), one who wins first place in a game or contest. *n.*

charge (chärj), rush at; attack. *v.*

chat ter (chat′ər), talk constantly in a quick, foolish way. *v.*

chit (chit), a saucy, bold girl. *n.*

coarse (kôrs), not fine; made up of fairly large parts: *coarse sand. adj.*

cob ble stone (kob′əl stōn), a rounded stone that was formerly much used in paving. *n.*

col lar (kol′ər), leather or metal band for a dog's neck. *n.*

col o ny (kol′ə nē), a group of people who leave their own country and go to settle in another land, but remain citizens of their own country. *n.*

colt (kōlt), young horse, donkey, etc. A male horse until it is four or five years old is a colt. *n.*

com mand (kə mand′), an order. *n.*

com mit tee (kə mit′ē), group of persons appointed or elected to do some special thing. *n.*

con cert (kon′sėrt), musical entertainment. *n.*

con gre ga tion (kong′grə gā′shən), a gathering of people for worship. *n.*

con quer (kong′kər), get the better of; overcome by force. *v.*

con tin ue (kən tin′ū), keep up; not stop. *v.*

con tral to (kən tral′tō), 1. lowest woman's voice. 2. part to be sung by lowest woman's voice. 3. person who sings this part. *n.*

cour age (kėr′ij), bravery. *n.*

crack le (krak′əl), a slight, sharp sound. *n.*

Cri mea (krī mē′a), large peninsula of Russia extending into the Black Sea from the North. *n.*

curl (kėrl), rise in rings. *v.*

dain ty (dān′tē), little; delicate and pretty. *adj.*

dair y (dãr′ē), a room or building where milk and cream are kept and made into butter and cheese. *n.*

dam age (dam′ij), to harm or injure so as to make less valuable or useful; hurt. *v.*

dan de li on (dan′də lī′ən), a common weed with deeply notched leaves and bright-yellow flowers that bloom in the spring. *n.*

---

hat, āge, cãre, fär; let, ēqual, tėrm; it, īce; hot, ōpen, ôrder; oil, out; cup, pùt, rüle, ūse; ch, child; ng, long; th, thin; ⊤H, then; zh, measure; ə represents *a* in about, *e* in taken, *i* in pencil, *o* in lemon, *u* in circus.

day dream (dā′ drēm′), dreamy thinking of pleasant things. *n.*

de ci sion (di sizh′ən), deciding; judgment; making up one's mind. *n.*

de light ful (di līt′fəl), giving joy; very pleasing. *adj.*

de part ment (di pärt′mənt), a separate part of some whole. *n.*

de ter mined (di tėr′mənd), with one's mind firmly made up. *adj.*

dif fer ent (dif′ər ənt), not alike. *adj.*

dif fi cult (dif′ə kult), hard to do or understand. *adj.*

dis ap pear (dis′ə pēr′), pass from sight or from existence. *v.*

dis ease (də zēz′), sickness; illness. *n.*

dis play (dis plā′), a planned showing of a thing, for some special purpose. *n.*

dis turb (dis tėrb′), break in upon with noise or change. *v.*

draw er (drôr), a box with handles built to slide in and out of a table, desk, or bureau. *n.*

drow sy (drou′zē), sleepy. *adj.*

e con o my (i kon′ə mē), making the most of what one has. *n.*

e lec tric (i lek′trik), run by electricity. *adj.*

el e men ta ry (el′ə men′tə-rē), introductory; dealing with simpler parts. *adj.*

el e va tor (el′ə vā′tər), machine for carrying people or things up and down in a building. *n.*

e nam el (i nam′əl), glasslike substance melted and then cooled to make a hard, smooth surface. *n.*

end less (end′lis), having no end. *adj.*

en er gy (en′ər jē), vigor; will to work. *n.*

en rage (en rāj′), make very angry. *v.*

en roll (en rōl′), become a member. *v.*

en ve lope (en′və lōp), a folded and gummed paper cover in which a letter or anything flat may be mailed. *n.*

er rand (er′ənd), a trip to do something. *n.*

es ca la tor (es′kə lā′tər), moving stairway. *n.*

es tate (es tāt′), a large piece of land. *n.*

eve ry one (ev′rē wun), each one; everybody. *pron.*

ex am ine (eg zam′ən), look at closely and carefully. *v.*

ex cite ment (ek sīt′mənt), aroused or stirred up state. *n.*

ex er cise (ek′sər sīz), something that gives practice. *n.*

ex pect (eks pekt′), think something will come or happen. *v.*

fa ble (fā′bəl), a story that is made up to teach a lesson. *n.*

fawn (fôn), deer less than a year old. *n.*

feast (fēst), take delight in; delight: *We feasted our eyes on the sunset. v.*

field (fēld), surface on which some emblem is pictured. *n.*

fin ger (fing′gər), touch or handle with the fingers. *v.*

fire place (fīr′ plās′), place built to hold a fire. *n.*

flag staff (flag′ staf′), pole from which a flag is flown. *n.*

flash light (flash′ līt′), a portable electric light. *n.*

flus ter (flus′tər), excite, confuse. *v.*

foe (fō), enemy, *n.*

fore man (fôr′ mən), man in charge of a group of workmen. *n.*

fore see (fôr sē′), see or know beforehand. *v.*

frail (frāl), 1. slender and not very strong; weak. 2. easily broken or giving way. *adj.*

free dom (frē′ dəm), liberty; power to do, say, or think as one pleases. *n.*

friend ship (frend′ ship), state of being friends; a liking between friends. *n.*

frond (frond), the leaf of a fern. *n.*

ful fill (fül fil′), carry out (a promise, prophecy, etc.). *v.*

fu ry (fūr′ē), rage; a storm of anger. *n.*

ga zette (gə zet′), a newspaper. *n.*

gen er ous (jen′ər əs), willing to share with others; unselfish. *adj.*

gig gle (gig′əl), laugh in a silly or undignified way. *v.*

gov ern ment (guv′ərn mənt), the system of ruling a country. *n.*

gov er nor (guv′ər nər), official elected as the executive head of a state of the United States. *n.*

greet (grēt), address in welcome. *v.*

guide (gīd), show the way. *v.*

gush (gush), rush out suddenly; pour out. *v.*

habit (hab′it), custom. *n.*

hard ship (härd′ ship), something hard to bear. *n.*

hard ware (härd′ wār′), articles made from metal. Locks, hinges, nails, screws, knives, etc., are hardware. *n.*

harsh (härsh), cruel; unfeeling. *adj.*

heav en (hev′ən), the upper air in which clouds float,

---

hat, āge, cāre, fär; let, ēqual, tėrm; it, īce; hot, ōpen, ôrder; oil, out; cup, pu̇t, rüle, ūse; ch, child; ng, long; th, thin; ŦH, then; zh, measure; ə represents *a* in about, *e* in taken, *i* in pencil, *o* in lemon, *u* in circus.

winds blow, and birds fly;
the sky. *n.*

her o ine   (her'ō in),   very
brave girl or woman. *n.*

hes i tate (hez'ə tāt), hold
back; be undecided. *v.*

home ward (hōm' wərd), toward home. *adv.*

hos pi tal (hos'pi təl), a place
for the care of the sick or
wounded. *n.*

house (hous), an assembly for
making laws. In the United
States the House of Repre-
sentatives is the lower house
of Congress. *n.*

hu mid i ty (hū mid'ə tē), 1.
moisture;   dampness.   2.
amount of moisture in the
air. *n.*

hy drant (hī'drənt), an upright cylinder or street fix-
ture with a valve for drawing water directly from a
main. Hydrants are used to
get water to put out fires,
wash streets, etc. *n.*

im mor tal (i môr'təl), living
forever. *adj.*

in born (in' bôrn'), born in a
person: *inborn talent for
drawing. adj.*

in de pend ent   (in'di pen'-
dənt), needing, wishing, or
getting no help from others.
adj.

in ning (in'ing), the turn of
one side in a game. *n.*

in sist (in sist'), keep firmly
to some demand, statement,

or way of thinking: *Mother
insists that we wash before
eating. v.*

in sur ance (in shür'əns), the
business of insuring prop-
erty, life, etc. *n.*

in ter fere (in'tər fēr'), disturb the affairs of others;
busy oneself with or in other
people's things   or   affairs
without being needed or
asked. *v.*

is land (ī'lənd), a body of land
surrounded by water. *n.*

jack rab bit (jak rab'it), large
hare   of   western   North
America, having very long
legs and ears. *n.*

kind ness   (kīnd'nis),   kind
treatment. *n.*

la dy like (lā'dē līk'), suit-
able for a lady. *adj.*

laun dry (lôn'drē), a room or
building where clothes are
washed and ironed. *n.*

law yer (lô'yər), person who
knows the laws and gives
advice about matters of law
or acts for another person in
court. *n.*

ledge (lej), a shelf or ridge of
rock. *n.*

li brar i an (lī brãr'ē ən), person in charge of a library. *n.*

li brar y (lī′brer′ē), a room or building in which a collection of books is kept. *n.*

light ning (līt′ning), a flash of electricity in the sky. *n.*

li lac (lī′lək), a shrub with clusters of fragrant, pale pinkish-purple or white blossoms. *n.*

lone some (lōn′ səm), feeling lonely. *adj.*

look out (lùk′ out′), place from which to watch. *n.*

loud-speak er (loud′spēk′-ər), a device for increasing sound. *n.*

lul la by (lul′ə bī), song for singing to a child in a cradle. *n.*

lu mi nous (lü′mə nəs), full of light; bright. *adj.*

lurch (lèrch), lean or roll suddenly to one side. *v.*

mail box (māl′ boks′), public box from which mail is collected. *n.*

mail car ri er (māl kar′ē ər), person who carries or delivers mail. *n.*

man ag er (man′ij ər), a person who controls, handles, or directs. *n.*

may or (mā′ər), the man at the head of a city or town government. *n.*

mem o ry (mem′ə rē), something that is remembered. *n.*

me ter (mē′tər), something that measures, or records. *n.*

mid night (mid′ nīt′), twelve o'clock at night. *n.*

might y (mīt′ē), powerful; strong. *adj.*

mistress (mis′tris), woman who is at the head of the household. *n.*

mock ing bird (mok′ing bèrd′), a songbird that imitates the notes of other birds. *n.*

mo tion (mō′shən), make a movement, as of the hand or head, to show one's meaning. *v.*

mouth piece (mouth′pēs′), the part of a pipe, horn, telephone, etc. that is placed in or at the mouth. *n.*

mul ber ry (mul′ber′ē), any of various trees such as the *American mulberry*, that yields a berrylike fruit. *n.*

mu se um (mū zē′əm), the building or rooms in which a collection of objects illustrating science, history, art, or other subjects is kept. *n.*

neck tie (nek′ tī′), a band or tie worn around the neck and tied in front. *n.*

night in gale (nīt′ ən gāl), a small reddish-brown bird of Europe. *n.*

nov el (nov′əl), a story with

---

hat, āge, cãre, fär; let, ēqual, tèrm; it, īce; hot, ōpen, ôrder; oil, out; cup, pùt, rüle, ūse; ch, child; ng, long; th, thin; ~~TH~~, then; zh, measure; ə represents *a* in about, *e* in taken, *i* in pencil, *o* in lemon, *u* in circus.

characters and a plot, long enough to fill one or more books. Novels are usually about people, scenes, and happenings such as might be met in real life. *n.*

of fi cial (ə fish′əl), having authority. *adj.*

op er a (op′ər ə), play that is mostly sung, with costumes, scenery, acting, and music to go with the singing. *n.*

o rig i nal (ə rij′ə nəl), first; earliest. *adj.*

out er (out′ər) on the outside. *adj.*

o ver alls (ō′vər ôlz′), loose trousers worn over clothes to keep them clean. *n.*

o ver due (ō′vər dü′), due some time ago. *adj.*

own er ship (ōn′ər ship), the possessing (of something). *n.*

pack (pak), a number of dogs kept together for hunting. *n.*

pant (pant), breathe hard and quickly. *v.*

pan ther (pan′thər), a leopard. *n.*

par a chute (par′ə shüt), an apparatus somewhat like an umbrella, made of nylon or silk, used in descending safely through the air from a great height. *n.*

par tic u lar (pər tik′ü lər), single; apart from others; considered separately. *adj.*

part ner (pärt′nər), one who shares. *n.*

pas teur i za tion (pas′chər ə zā′shən), process of heating milk, etc., to a high enough temperature to destroy harmful bacteria. *n.*

pas tor (pas′tər), minister in charge of a church. *n.*

pawn shop (pôn′ shop′), the shop of a man who lends money on articles that are left with him as security for a loan. *n.*

peb ble (peb′əl), a small stone, usually worn and rounded by being rolled about by water. *n.*

peer (pēr), look closely to see clearly, as a near-sighted person does. *v.*

pen man ship (pen′ mən ship), handwriting. *n.*

pierce (pērs), make a hole by pushing through. *v.*

pinch hitter, one who bats for another baseball player when a hit is badly needed. *n.*

pi rate (pī′rit), robber on the sea. *n.*

pit y (pit′ē), feel sympathy; sorrow for the suffering of others. *v.*

plunge (plunj), rush; dash. *v.*

po et ry (pō′it rē), poems. *n.*

po lite (pə līt′), behaving

properly; having or showing good manners. *adj.*

pol ly wog (pol'ē wog), tadpole. *n.*

poor house (pür' hous'), a house in which very poor persons live at public expense. *n.*

pop u lar (pop'u lər), liked by others. *adj.*

post er (pōs'tər), large printed sheet put up in a public place. *n.*

post mas ter (pōst' mas'tər), person in charge of a post office. *n.*

pot hook (pot' hůk'), an S-shaped stroke in writing, especially one made by children in learning to write. *n.*

pounce (pouns), jump suddenly and seize. *v.*

prac ti cal (prak'tə kəl), having to do with action or practice rather than thought or theory: *Earning a living is a practical matter. adj.*

prim (prim), stiffly precise, neat, proper, or formal. *adj.*

pri ma don na (prē'mə don'ə), principal woman singer in an opera. *n.*

pris on er (priz'ən ər), person taken by the enemy who is kept shut up against his will. *n.*

prize[1] (prīz), a reward worth working for. *n.*

prize[2] (prīz), value highly. *v.*

pro fes sion al (prə fesh'ən-əl), making a business or trade of something others do for pleasure. *adj.*

prop (prop), hold up by placing a support under or against. *v.*

prove (prüv), try out; test; put to a test. *v.*

pub lic (pub'lik), all the people. *n.*

pub lish (pub'lish), prepare and offer (a book, paper, map, piece of music, etc.) for sale and distribution. *v.*

pub lish er (pub'lish ər), person or company whose business is to print and sell books, magazines, etc. *n.*

punch (punch), pierce a hole in: *The train conductor punches tickets. v.*

pu pil (pū'pəl), one who is learning in school or is being taught by someone. *n.*

pur ple (pėr'pəl), a dark color made by mixing red and blue. *n.*

quiv er (kwiv'ər), tremble; shake; shiver. *v.*

rac coon (ra kün'), a small, grayish animal with a bushy ringed tail, that eats flesh,

---

hat, āge, cãre, fär; let, ēqual, tėrm; it, īce; hot, ōpen, ôrder; oil, out; cup, půt, rüle, ūse; ch, child; ng, long; th, thin; ŦH, then; zh, measure; ə represents *a* in about, *e* in taken, *i* in pencil, *o* in lemon, *u* in circus.

279

lives mostly in trees, and is active at night. *n.*

rack et (rak′it), loud noise; din. *n.*

re al ize (rē′əl īz), understand. *v.*

re cite (ri sīt′), say over; repeat. *v.*

reg is ter (rej′is tər), have one's name written in a list or record. *v.*

re join (rē join′), join again. *v.*

rep re sent a tive (rep′ri zen′tə tiv), person appointed to act or speak for others. *n.*

right (rīt), something that is due to a person. *n.*

ri val (rī′vəl), person who wants and tries to get the same thing as another. *n.*

round up (round′ up′), act of driving or bringing cattle together from long distances. *n.*

route (rüt or rout), way to go. *n.*

rus tle (rus′əl), move something so that it makes a sound such as leaves make when moved by the wind. *v.*

sci en tist (sī′ən tist), person who knows much about science. *n.*

scis sors (siz′ərz), a tool for cutting that has two sharp blades fastened so that they will move toward each other. *n.*

scram ble (skram′bəl), make one's way by climbing, crawling, etc. *v.*

sea shore (sē′shôr′), land along the sea. *n.*

sea weed (sē′ wēd′), any plant or plants growing in the sea. *n.*

sep a rate (sep′ə rit), apart from others. *adj.*

se ri ous (sēr′ē əs), thoughtful. *adj.*

set (set), put in the right condition for use: *The doctor set Tom's leg. v.*

se vere (sə vēr′), very strict. *adj.*

shaft (shaft), the long, slender stem of an arrow, spear, etc. *n.*

shelf (shelf), a thin, flat piece of wood fastened to a wall or frame to hold things such as books. *n.*

shiv er (shiv′ər), shake with cold, fear, etc. *v.*

short stop (shôrt′ stop′), baseball player between second and third base. *n.*

shove (shuv), to push; move forward or along by force from behind. *v.*

si ren (sī′rən), a kind of whistle that makes a loud piercing sound. *n.*

sketch (skech), a short description or story or play. *n.*

skin (skin), take the skin off: *The hunter skinned the deer. v.*

slot (slot), a small, narrow opening. *n.*

snap per (snap'ər), a red fish of tropical seas used for food. *n.*

snick er (snik'ər), a sly or silly laugh. *n.*

some one (sum' wun), some person. *pron.*

some times (sum' tīmz), now and then. *adv.*

soot (süt), black substance in the smoke from burning coal, wood, oil, etc. Soot makes smoke dark and collects on the inside of chimneys. *n.*

sort (sôrt), separate from others: *The farmer sorted out the best apples for eating. v.*

spe cial (spesh'əl), unusual; more than ordinary. *adj.*

speck (spek), small spot. *n.*

spi ral (spī'rəl), coiled. *adj.*

sprain (sprān), injure (a joint or muscle) by a sudden twist. *v.*

spring (spring), to leap or jump. *v.*

squad car (skwod kär), a police patrol car that keeps in touch with headquarters by special equipment. *n.*

squash (skwosh), a vegetable that grows on a vine. *n.*

squirm (skwėrm), wriggle; twist. *v.*

starve (stärv), die or suffer because of hunger. *v.*

stor y (stô'rē), the set of rooms on the same level or floor of a building: *The house has two stories. n.*

streak (strēk), a long thin mark or line. **Like a streak** means very fast: *The dog ran like a streak across the lawn. n.*

stream (strēm), flow; move steadily; move swiftly. *v.*

strug gle (strug'əl), make great efforts with the body. *v.*

stud y (stud'ē), 1. deep thought. 2. examine carefully. 3. try to learn. *n. v.*

sub urb (sub'ėrb), town or village just outside a city or town. *n.*

sug ges tion (səg jes'chən), thought or plan brought to the attention of another. *n.*

sun down (sun' doun'), sunset. *n.*

sun-up (sun' up'), sunrise. *n.*

sup port (sə pôrt'), provide for: *A healthy man should support his family. v.*

swift (swift), quick; rapid. *adj.*

swish (swish), move with a hissing sound. *v.*

tar get (tär'git), thing aimed at. A target is often a circle, but anything may be used as a target. *n.*

taxi cab (tak'sē kab'), automobile for hire with a meter

---

hat, āge, cãre, fär; let, ēqual, tėrm; it, īce; hot, ōpen, ôrder; oil, out; cup, pùt, rüle, ūse; ch, child; ng, long; th, thin; ᴛʜ, then; zh, measure; ə represents *a* in about, *e* in taken, *i* in pencil, *o* in lemon, *u* in circus.

to record the amount to be paid. *n.*

tel e phone (tel′ə fōn), a means of transmitting sound by electricity. *n.*

te pee (tē′pē), tent of the American Indians. *n.*

the a ter (thē′ə tər), place where plays are acted. *n.*

tim id (tim′id), shy. *adj.*

tip toe (tip′ tō′), walk on tips of toes. *v.*

tom boy (tom′ boi′), girl who likes to play boys′ games. *n.*

tongue (tung), the movable piece of flesh in the mouth. *n.*

tongue-tied (tung′ tīd′), unable to speak because of shyness, embarrassment, etc. *adj.*

ton sil (ton′səl), either of the two small oval masses of tissue on the sides of the throat, just back of the mouth. *n.*

tooth paste (tüth′ pāst′), paste used in cleaning the teeth. *n.*

track (trak), footprint. *n.*

traf fic (traf′ik), people, automobiles, wagons, ships, etc., coming and going along a way of travel. *n.*

treas ure (trezh′ər), 1. anything that is much valued: *The silver teapot is the old lady′s chief treasure.* 2. to value highly: *She treasures that doll more than all her other toys. n. v.*

tri al (trī′əl), process of trying or testing. *n.*

tro phy (trō′fē), memorial of victory; prize. *n.*

trudge (truj), walk in a tired manner or with effort. *v.*

true (trü), in an exact or accurate manner. *adv.*

twin kle (twing′kəl), shine with quick little gleams. *v.*

twitch (twich), move with a quick jerk. *v.*

um pire (um′pīr), a person who rules on the plays in a game. *n.*

un a ble (un ā′bəl), not able. *adj.*

un der ground (un′dər-ground′), beneath the surface of the ground. *adv.*

u ni form (ū′nə fôrm), clothes that are the same in style, color, worn by members of a group for a particular reason. *n.*

u nite (ū nīt′), join together. *v.*

up hol ster y (up hōl′stər ē), coverings, cushions, for furniture. *n.*

up stairs (up′ stārz′), on an upper floor. *adv.*

wail (wāl), cry loud and long because of grief or pain. *v.*

whim per (hwim′pər), cry with low, broken sounds in

the way that a sick child or dog does. *v.*

whis tle (hwis′əl), make a clear, shrill sound. *v.*

win try (win′trē), like winter. *adj.*

wound (wünd), injure by cutting, stabbing, shooting, etc.; hurt. *v.*

wres tling (res′ling), sport or contest in which each of two opponents tries to throw or

force the other to the ground. *n.*

yes ter day (yes′tər dē or yes′tər dā), the day before today. *n.*

zoom (züm), move suddenly. *v.*

---

hat, āge, cãre, fär; let, ēqual, tèrm; it, īce; hot, ōpen, ôrder; oil, out; cup, pùt, rüle, ūse; ch, child; ng, long; th, thin; ℋℋ, then; zh, measure; ə represents *a* in about, *e* in taken, *i* in pencil, *o* in lémon, *u* in circus.

Acknowledgments

Grateful acknowledgment is made for the following stories and poems to authors and publishers for permission to adapt and use their original or copyrighted material.

"Autumn Woods" from *A World to Know* by James S. Tippett, by permission of Martha K. Tippett.

"Boats Sail on the River" by Christina Rossetti from *Sing-Song,* copyright 1930 by The Macmillan Company, by permission of the publisher.

"Gray Fox and the Eagles" by Claire Duter, copyright 1952 by *Story Parade, Inc.;* reprinted and adapted by permission.

"Shore" from *Menagerie* by Mary Britton Miller, by permission of the author.

"The Hairy Dog" from *Pillicock Hill* by Herbert Asquith, by permission of the publishers, Oxford University Press and William Heinemann Ltd.

"The Park" from *I Live in a City* by James S. Tippett, by permission of Martha K. Tippett.

Illustrations: Allan and Ruth Eitzen, Anne Gayler, Gisela Jordan, Tim H. Lofton, Elsie Jane McCorkell, Albert F. Michini, W. Kirtman Plummer, Betsy Roosen, Roland V. Shutts, Carol Wilde, George Wilde, Francis Chauncey.

Cover design: Phil Rath.